NURSING STUDENTS WITH DISABILITIES

CHANGE THE COURSE

DONNA CAROL MAHEADY,

ED.D., C.P.N.P., RN

ISBN: 0-9309589-12-8

Cover design by BooksJustBooks.com
Book design by BooksJustBooks.com
Book Edited by Joseph M. Valenzano III, M.A.

Exceptional Parent Press
65 East Route 4
River Edge, NJ 07661

Visit our website at http://www.eparent.com, or view our book
collection at http://www.eplibrary.com

Printed in the United States of America

This book is dedicated to my daughter, Lauren,
who continues to teach me to live life
with hope, grace, laughter and celebration.

Kindness is the language which
the deaf can hear and the blind can see.
—Mark Twain

ACKNOWLEDGMENTS

I would like to acknowledge the following people for assisting me in the creation of this book: the nursing students who shared their stories, Tom Gili for his ongoing support and encouragement, Dr. Harold Turner for his advice and counsel, Joe Valenzano for his belief in me and the book, and Susan Matt, Nancy Johanson, and the staff at Exceptional Parent for their editorial skill. Thank you all very much.

CONTENTS

A Brief Note

On November 18, 1995, Itzhak Perlman, the violinist, walked slowly across the stage of Avery Fisher Hall at Lincoln Center in New York City. Audiences were accustomed to watching him majestically traverse stages using his crutches, and this one was no exception. When he reached his chair, he slowly lowered himself onto it and placed the crutches on the floor at his side. He loosened the clasps on his leg braces, tucked one foot to the side of the chair and extended the other one forward. He picked up the violin, which was resting on a conveniently positioned stand, placed it under his chin, nodded to the conductor and proceeded to play. But this particular night, something went wrong. Just as he finished the first few bars, one of the violin strings broke, snapping like gunfire and landing across the stage.

The audience expected him to refasten the clasps on his braces, pick up the crutches, and leave the stage in search of another violin or string. Instead, Perlman waited only a moment, with closed eyes, before signaling the conductor to begin again. The sounds of the orchestra filled the concert hall, and Perlman's violin magic captivated the audience. He played with intensity, passion, and purity. The audience could almost visualize him modulating and recomposing the piece in his head. Musicians would probably say that it is impossible to play a symphonic work with only three strings, but this particular night, Itzhak Perlman refused to recognize that.

When he finished playing, the people in the audience rose and cheered. Perlman smiled, wiped the sweat from his brow, and raised his bow to quiet them. He spoke in a quiet, reverent tone. "You know, sometimes it is the artist's task to find out how much music he can still make with what he has left."

PREFACE

In the early 1980s, I was teaching nursing courses in a baccalaureate degree program in Florida. One day, an application from a prospective student with a disability was presented at a faculty meeting. The student was a registered nurse with an associate degree in nursing, and she was applying to the baccalaureate program. After years of practice as a nurse, she had suffered an injury that resulted in her need to use a wheelchair. The faculty members were quite concerned about her limitations, particularly about her ability to provide safe nursing care and to meet the goals and objectives of the program. Clinical agencies were contacted regarding the needs of this student. Every hospital and clinic was concerned about patient care, safety, liability, accessibility, and the possible reactions of patients and staff members. I had my share of doubts as well.

Over the ensuing years, I have worked with numerous nursing students with disabilities, some with learning disabilities and others with hearing loss. None of them formally disclosed their disability to the nursing program. The students' disclosures to me came with time and the development of trust. I continue to wonder how much better their educational experiences would have been if they had disclosed their problems to the nursing program and received the support and accommodations they needed. I am still concerned about patient safety, and I struggle with questions about how we can simultaneously support nursing students with disabilities, maintain confidentiality, and promote safe nursing care.

Little did I know, when working with these students, that the birth of my daughter would change many of my views on nursing, disability, and education. Lauren is a teenager who embraces life with many challenges, including mental retardation, a seizure disorder, pervasive development disorder, obsessive-compulsive tendencies and limited speech. She has opened my eyes and heart to the gifts that people with disabilities bring to those they encounter or befriend. She has been the driving force behind this book.

Often, parents of a child with a disability live the experience of their child. I am one of those parents. I have navigated the health care system, battled with the school system, and fought with insurance companies for therapies Lauren has needed. I have advocated tirelessly for her right to be included in recreation, camp, and community activities. My calendar is filled with the committee and board meetings I attend while advocating not only for Lauren's rights, but for the human rights of all people with disabilities. I am fluent in the disability and special education language. Words like accommodations, modifications, inclusion, and support are as familiar to me as nursing terminology.

While teaching, practicing, and raising my daughter, I worked on my doctoral degree in education. It was a long road, and the journey to complete my dissertation was more than a challenge. My dissertation topic was related to the experiences of nursing students with disabilities (Maheady, 1999). Through my research, I interviewed and observed nursing students with a wide variety of disabilities. The stories about their experiences were powerful. After I completed the dissertation, I committed myself to do more with the information.

Nursing students with disabilities present new challenges to nursing education and practice. Some of my views may not be popular— like many new ideas—but the issues must be addressed. There are many ways to meet the learning needs of these students. I propose the necessity for student disclosure of a disability, as well as utilization of an individualized nursing education program. This recommendation does not view the nursing student with a disability as "less than whole." Rather, it recognizes that if a nursing student with a hearing loss is required to hear heart and lung sounds, then accommodations must be made in order to compensate for the hearing loss and to maintain patient safety.

Disclosure of a disability is essential for students to obtain the accommodations they need as well as to promote safe nursing care. As you will learn, however, disclosure often comes with great consequences to the student. From my experiences as an advocate for people with disabilities, I have learned that institutional change only comes when a person with a disability asks for the change. It is unlikely that a nursing program will actively recruit students with disabilities, unless it is a program funded for that purpose.

The following chapters include first person accounts from eight nursing students with a variety of disabilities. The students discuss the admission process to a nursing program, the risks of disclosure, and accommodations and reactions from professors, patients, and fellow students. The stories are followed by "questions to ponder" and examples of individualized nursing education programs that might have been developed. Commentary on significant points of interest or concern is also included, particularly when related to special equipment, harassment, legal issues, and transportation.

This book is a tribute to nursing students with disabilities. It showcases their unique abilities and remarkable determination to achieve their goals. Their personal sacrifices will inspire strength in other students and give nursing educators, guidance and vocational rehabilitation counselors and disability service staff greater insight. Nursing students with disabilities will change the course.

INTRODUCTION

There was a time when Caucasian and African-American nurses were educated separately in the United States. Today, our college and university nursing programs embrace students of both genders as well as those who are rich in ethnic diversity. This is a stark contrast to the past, where nursing schools were filled with predominantly Caucasian women. The course has changed.

There was also a time when nurses were thought to be people without disabilities. In reality, this may have never been true, since, historically, nurses with various disabilities did not disclose them. Gradually, students with disabilities have been applying to nursing programs, openly disclosing their problems, graduating, passing national licensing examinations, and going on to practice their profession. While these changes are due to many factors, the students' spirits and determination to follow their dreams have been paramount. Additional support has come from legislation that protects their rights, and from the current social and political climate surrounding inclusion of persons with disabilities in all walks of life. The course is, indeed, changing.

Nursing educators are addressing important questions and issues, regarding the nursing education of students with disabilities, including the implications of admission decisions on the college or university, faculty members, other students, and patients. For example, a nursing program may receive an application from a student with a hearing loss. If the student is admitted, he or she will need accommodations, which may include tape-recorded lectures, a note taker, a sign language interpreter, or front row seating in the classroom. In clinical settings, nursing instructors, staff members and patients may need to speak directly to the student's face. The student may be unable to hear call bells, intravenous pump monitors, and calls for help from patients. Accommodations and equipment, such as an amplified stethoscope, may be necessary, to enable this student to provide safe nursing care.

Another applicant for admission to a nursing program may have an above-the-elbow amputation. If admitted to the program, this student may not require accommodations in the classroom, but may have difficulty drawing up medications in syringes, giving injections, and performing various procedures in clinical settings, such as catheterization and tracheotomy suctioning. Obviously, accommodations will be necessary for this student to acquire these skills.

A student with short stature may apply to a nursing program, and, if accepted, will not require accommodations in the classroom, but may be unable to reach medications in the medication room without a stepstool. The student may be unable to ambulate with a tall patient in the hallway or to assist with procedures in the hospital treatment room without special accommodations.

In 1973, the Rehabilitation Act Section 504 was passed, stating: "No otherwise qualified handicapped individual in the United States...shall solely, by reason of this handicap, be excluded from the participation in, be denied the benefits of, or be subjected to discrimination under any program or activity receiving federal financial assistance." It goes on to state that "qualified disabled individuals cannot be subject to discrimination in educational programs. A qualified disabled individual is defined as one who meets the academic and technical standards required for admission. These persons may have disabilities such as, but not limited to, the following: (a) blindness or visual impairments, (b) cerebral palsy, (c) chronic illnesses, (d) deafness or hearing impairments, (e) drug or alcohol addiction, (f) epilepsy or seizure disorders, (g) mental retardation, (h) orthopedic handicap, (i) specific learning disability, (j) speech disorder, or (k) spinal cord or traumatic brain injury."

In 1990 another landmark piece of legislation, the Americans with Disabilities Act, was passed. It serves as an omnibus civil rights law that prohibits discrimination on the basis of disability by, among others, entities providing public and private preschool, elementary, secondary, and postsecondary education. It also prohibits discrimination on the basis of disability in employment, state and local government, public accommodations, commercial facilities, transportation, and telecommunications.

These laws were enacted to level the playing field for people with disabilities. The intention is clear, but the actual standards and terminology are not so clear. Different people interpret the laws differently, and the courts have progressively chiseled away at the laws (Matt, 2003).

Students who applied to nursing programs have filed lawsuits involving alleged discrimination on the basis of disability. In some cases, the court has ruled in favor of the student and, in other cases, in favor of the institution. In the monumental Davis v. Southeastern Community College (1979) case, a student with a severe hearing impairment was denied admission to the nursing program. The U.S. Supreme Court upheld the college's decision and ruled that a law forbidding bias against handicapped persons does not bar colleges from requiring "reasonable physical qualifications" of students, in programs where such qualifications play an important role.

In another case, a nursing student who suffered from Crohn's Disease was refused admission to a nursing program. The school stated that, due to her condition, she would miss an excessive number of classes. The court ruled that the school's decision was unjustified (Manson, 1982).

To date, no national standards exist regarding admission guidelines for students with disabilities. Most programs require written documentation of a disability, in order to determine appropriate accommodations. Decisions are made on a case-by-case basis. This approach offers students the benefits of individual assessment, but the lack of general admission criteria may cause inconsistencies in the admission process.

A nursing program is required to provide reasonable accommodations, but is not required to make modifications that would substantially alter the nature or requirements of the program. Admission guidelines at some programs may include specific physical attributes needed to provide safe nursing care. They may include attributes such as the physical ability to perform cardiopulmonary resuscitation (CPR), enough visual acuity to identify cyanosis, the manual dexterity to draw up solutions in a syringe, enough hearing ability to understand normal speech without viewing the speaker's face, or the emotional health required to exercise sound judgment.

Other programs may use core performance standards that address communication, motor skills, hearing, visual and tactile abilities. These standards may include the ability to hear monitor alarms, auscultatory sounds, cries for help, and the ability to move from room to room and to maneuver in small spaces. Students will find differences in the admission guidelines of nursing programs, but, as a general rule, they will need to be able to perform all of the essential functions of the program, with or without accommodations.

In 1992, the Board of Directors of the Southern Council on Collegiate Education for Nursing (SCCEN) developed guidelines for nursing education programs, in compliance with the ADA. The guidelines were designed to assist nursing educators in their development of proactive responses in support of students covered by the ADA. Core performance standards for admission and progression were identified, and addressed (a) critical thinking; (b) interpersonal; (c) communication; (d) mobility; (e) motor skills; (f) hearing; (g) visual; and (h) tactile issues (Davis, Bowlin, Hassard & Fitch, 1992).

Each standard had an example of an activity that a student would be required to perform while enrolled in a typical college or university nursing program. For example, a hearing activity included the standard of auditory ability sufficient enough to monitor and assess health needs, such as hearing monitors, emergency signals, auscultatory sounds, and cries for help. A mobility activity included the standard of physical abilities to move from one room to another and to maneuver in small spaces. Other necessary activities included the ability to move around in patients' rooms, work-spaces and treatment areas, and to administer cardiopulmonary resuscitation (Davis, Bowlin, Hassard & Fitch, 1992).

Nursing educators and students continue to ask questions such as "What guidelines should be used for admission of a student with a disability?"; "How can the needs of the student be accommodated without compromising the quality of the educational program?"; "What accommodations will facilitate successful outcomes?"; "How can nursing students with disabilities provide safe patient care?"; "What problems can faculty anticipate?"; How can confidentiality be maintained?"; and " Will nursing students with disabilities experience problems in passing national board licensing examinations and gaining employment in the field?"

At the present time we can look to pioneer nursing students with disabilities to answer some of these questions. There is much to be learned from their experiences. Students who are considering a career in nursing, as well as nurses who become disabled later in their careers, can learn from the personal accounts of these pioneers.

In the following chapters, eight nursing students with disabilities tell their stories. Their disabilities include hearing loss, diabetes, Crohn's disease, back injury, and paraplegia. Names, gender, dates, and locations have been changed to protect their privacy, but their accounts are, nonetheless, painfully honest, and, sometimes disturbing. They share information about the admission process to a nursing program, the benefits and risks of disclosure, the particular accommodations that were helpful, and the reactions of faculty, patients and other students. They provide personal recommendations for other nursing students with disabilities and nursing faculty members. They offer encouragement for students considering a career in nursing, and shed light on the current controversies and concerns regarding patient safety.

Their stories share common threads of determination, hard work, and love for the profession. Their experiences signal the need for nursing educators to make academic environments more open to student disclosure of a disability, as well as to provide whatever accommodations are required to promote patient safety.

Following each narration, I present questions to ponder, a sample Individualized Nursing Education Program, and commentary on various issues, such as special equipment, harassment, legal issues, transportation, and uniforms. I conclude by identifying the responsibilities of students, guidance counselors, nursing programs, educators, and state boards of nursing to meet the needs of nursing students with disabilities. A resource section includes information about organizations, financial aid, legal resources, equipment and technology.

This material does not serve as a guarantee for admission to a nursing program, successful completion of the licensing examination, or employment as a nurse. Decisions will be made on case-by-case basis, by individual nursing programs, state boards of nursing, and employers, asked on the college or university admission guidelines, state nursing board regulations, Nurse Practice Acts, and the needs of each applicant.

ABBREVIATIONS

ADA- The Americans with Disabilities Act

AD- Associate Degree Program

ASAP- As soon as possible

BSN- Bachelor of Science Degree Program in Nursing

CART- Computer Assisted Real-time Transcription

CPR- Cardio-pulmonary resuscitation

CPT- Chest physiotherapy

EMT- Emergency Medical Technician

FAPE- Free Appropriate Public Education

GPA- Grade Point Average

GRE- Graduate Record Examination

ICU- Intensive Care Unit

IDEA- Individuals with Disabilities Education Act

IEP- Individualized Education Program

INEP- Individualized Nursing Education Program

IV- Intravenous

LPN- Licensed Practical Nurse

NCLEX- National Council Licensure Examination

NLN- National League for Nursing

OR- Operating Room

PDA- Personal Digital Assistant

SAT- Scholastic Aptitude Test

Nursing Students
with Disabilities

CHAPTER 1

PLANNING FOR SUCCESS
The Individualized Education Program

Children who receive special education and related services in public schools must have an Individualized Education Program (IEP). This is the cornerstone for providing a free and appropriate public education (FAPE) to students with disabilities, under the Individuals with Disabilities Education Act (IDEA) (formerly called P.L. 94-142 or the Education for all Handicapped Children Act of 1975). Although this legal mandate does not apply to students in postsecondary school, the overall structure or framework that is used, based on the student's individual needs, may be an approach that nursing educators and prospective nursing students should consider.

The 1997 amendments to IDEA call for several changes in the IEP development process that may be helpful as well. In July 2000, the Office of Special Education and Rehabilitative Services published "A Guide to the Individualized Education Program," which identifies the contents of the IEP required by the Individuals with Disabilities Act. The following sections provide information, with suggestions on how the framework might be adapted and applied to a student in higher education, particularly for a student in a nursing education program. The adapted Individualized Education Program will be called "Individualized Nursing Education Program."

Creating a Program

To create an effective Individualized Nursing Education Program for a nursing student, the student, faculty, and representatives from the college or university's Office of Students with Disabilities must come together for a close examination and analysis of the student's unique needs. An effective program will require teamwork, as every member of the team must cooperate in order to design a program that will ensure the student's success. All information should remain confidential, and all participants should receive a copy of the program. The particular format or appearance is not important, but what is important is that the format be as clear and useful as possible. In essence, the Individualized Nursing Education Program is a practical guide that will describe the student's needs and identify who is responsible for what, when, and where. This approach should facilitate accountability from every participant and assist with the evaluation of the student's performance.

The IDEA requires that the following italicized information be included in an Individualized Education Program (IEP) for children in public schools. Possibilities for application of this information with students in nursing education programs follow each section.

Current Performance

The IEP should contain information about how the student is doing in school (known as the present level of performance) and how the student's disability affects his or her involvement and progress in the curriculum.

Application to Nursing Education

This section could include the nursing student's grade point average (GPA), transcript of grades, SAT score, GRE score, letters of recommendation, evaluations, and observations from faculty members. It could also include a letter from the student's physician that explains the student's disability.

Annual Goals

The IEP should include goals that the student can reasonably accomplish in a year. The goals must be measurable and include benchmarks or short-term objectives.

Application to Nursing Education

The Individualized Nursing Education Program may need to include goals that can be accomplished within a semester or quarter of the nursing program's academic year. They should be measurable and include short-term objectives, or benchmarks. One example might be written as "the nursing student must receive a final passing grade (C or better) in Nursing 101, at the completion of the semester." A short-term goal or benchmark might be "the nursing student must achieve an average grade of C or better at mid-term, in Nursing 101."

Objectives should be specifically related to the student's disability. For instance, "the nursing student will purchase a special stethoscope," "the nursing student will demonstrate the ability to perform lung auscultation with an amplified stethoscope by mid-term," or "the nursing student will complete all make-up work, due to illness or hospitalization, by the end of the semester."

Special Education and Related Services

The Individualized Education Program lists the special education and related services to be provided to the student. This includes supplementary aids and services that the student needs. It also includes modifications (changes) to the program or supports for school personnel.

Application to Nursing Education

The Individualized Nursing Education Program should list the related services to be provided to the nursing student. The list might include supplementary aids and services and modifications to the program (e.g., a tutor, note taker, textbooks recorded on tape, a listening device, sign language, or oral interpreter). It might also include supports, such as access to a refrigerator to store medication, nurse availability, a place to either lie down or rest during the day, or access to priority (early) registration.

Technological Devices

The Individualized Education Program should consider whether the student requires assistive (sic) technology devices in order to meet his or her educational goals and access to the curriculum. An assistive technology device is broadly defined as any piece of equipment that is used to increase, maintain, or improve the functional capabilities of a student with a disability. Tools can be simple or complex.

Application to Nursing Education
The Individualized Nursing Education Program should consider technological devices, from calculators and tape recorders to voice recognition software and Optacons, to help the nursing student meet the goals of the curriculum.

Participation with Nondisabled Students
The Individualized Education Program must explain the extent to which the student will not participate with nondisabled (sic) students in the regular class and other school activities.

Application to Nursing Education
This issue will most likely not apply to nursing students. It would apply only if a number of nursing students with disabilities shared a class, laboratory, or clinical experience, separate from nursing students without disabilities.

Participation in State and District-Wide Tests
Most states and districts give achievement tests to children in certain grades. The Individualized Education Program must state modifications in the administration of these tests that the student will need. In the event that a test is not appropriate for the student, the Individualized Education Program must state why the test is not appropriate and how the student will be tested.

Application to Nursing Education
This section addresses the needs of a nursing student with a disability relating to the taking of examinations and tests given in courses within the nursing program or on National League for Nursing (NLN) examinations. The student might be allowed additional time to complete an examination, or allowed the use of a calculator or computer. The student might be given oral examinations or a modified test format, such as one with large print, an essay format, multiple-choice questions, or a case study.

Dates and Places

The IEP should state when services will begin, how often they will be provided, where they will be provided, and how long the services will last. The IEP should be reviewed at least once a year.

Application to Nursing Education

The Individualized Nursing Education Program should include information about a support or service that will be provided to a nursing student, for instance a note taker or sign language interpreter. This section should include the location of the service, the timeline, and who will provide it. For example, a nursing student might be provided with a note taker from the Office of Students with Disabilities for fifteen credit hours of theory courses, on the main campus, during the fall semester. The Individualized Nursing Education Program may need to be reviewed, and revised if necessary, every semester, quarter, or more often.

Transition Services Needs

When a student is age 14, the Individualized Education Program must address the courses he or she needs to take to reach his or her post-school goals.

Application to Nursing Education

This section of INEP should address additional courses that the nursing student with a disability needs, in order to reach professional goals. Include required courses, any remedial courses that would benefit the student, and recommendations for special equipment or technological aids.

Needed Transition Services

At the age of 16, the IEP must state what transition services are needed to help the student prepare for leaving school.

Application to Nursing Education

This part of an INEP might include transition services and supports that will assist the nursing student in preparation for the NCLEX examination and employment, later, as a nurse. It might include recommendations for tutoring, employment counseling, preceptorship programs, and (NCLEX) preparation courses.

Age of Majority
Beginning at least one year before the student reaches the age of majority, the IEP must include a statement that the student has been informed of any rights that will transfer to him or her at the age of majority. This is only needed in states that transfer rights at the age of majority.

Application to Nursing Education
The age of majority should not be an issue for students in nursing education programs.

Measuring Progress
The IEP must state how the student's progress will be measured and how parents will be informed of that progress.

Application to Nursing Education
Evaluation methods and time schedules, for determining whether or not the goals and objectives have been met, should be included in the INEP. Evaluation of the student's progress should include a consideration of examination results, the quality of written work and projects, and a demonstration of clinical skills. A mid-term and final evaluation should be written by the faculty member and signed by student. A meeting should be held at mid-term and at the end of the term, including the student, faculty members, dean, and a representative from the Office of Students with Disabilities. Final course grades should be sent through the mail.

● ● ●

In the following chapters, eight nursing students with disabilities share their experiences. Following each narrative is a sample of an individualized nursing education program that could have been developed for that particular student. It should be noted that the information presented in each account limits the comprehensive development of an individualized nursing education program, because the programs were developed based on the information provided by the student. More information would be needed, to develop an authentic and effective program. The sample programs are meant to serve only as a practical guide for both students and educators. In some situations, the samples may serve as a springboard for a discussion on what could work for a particular student and nursing program.

CHAPTER 2

MAKING THE RIGHT CAREER CHOICE
Nursing school with a hearing loss

Marion shares her journey through a BSN program in the South. She graduated and is now practicing as a nurse. Currently, she is attending graduate school. She has hearing loss in both ears. The higher ranges of sounds are missing completely, so she must wear hearing aids.

This may seem hard to believe, but when I applied to the baccalaureate program in nursing, I didn't think my hearing impairment would significantly affect the way I would work as a nurse. I didn't realize how important hearing was to being a nurse, until I arrived on campus, and I had no conscious intention to hide my disability. I had simply never been in a situation where it was a problem. In my previous college work, I had always offset my hearing loss by working hard, paying attention, and lip reading.

I have a hearing loss in both ears and have particular difficulty hearing female voices. The higher range is, for all practical purposes, missing. My hearing aids help to offset the problem, but there are still limitations. I can amplify sounds, but I can't selectively amplify sounds. At a certain point, when I turn the hearing aids up, the sound becomes more confusing than useful. That is the best way I can explain it. I don't hear consonants clearly; I know that someone is speaking, but I don't always hear what is being said. In other words, fifty, sixty, fifteen, and sixteen sound the same to me.

The onset of my hearing loss remains a mystery. I became aware of it as an adult. I was working in an office and noticed that when people turned around, I didn't hear the rest of their conversations. In some situations, I didn't hear anything. I had my ears checked. The people who did the hearing test were astounded that, at thirty years old, I could function as though I had no problem. After I was fitted with one hearing aid, I realized the full extent of my hearing loss. Now, I wear two hearing aids.

My father has a similar hearing loss, although it's not progressive. My dad got his hearing aids at the same time I did, so the amount of time he lived without hearing was long. When you function with a disability for years, you don't know there is another way, until someone says, "You're not hearing anything." Then, you learn how loud the world is. There are times that I remove the hearing aids, because I'm used to the world being quiet, and they can make me feel nervous. If I want to relax, I remove the hearing aids and go for a walk.

My whole family has the attitude, "You can do it; you have to do it. It's your responsibility to see that you get it done." Since they do not work in health care, they do not have a realistic picture of how much a nurse needs to hear. They would be the first to say, "If there's a better hearing aid, or if there's anything you need, we'll help you get it." On my mother's side of the family, there is an old saying that, "You can solve any problem, if you can throw enough money at it. It's your job to make that money!" My parents helped me with my tuition, though, to eliminate financial stress. I can't complain about family support.

My first degree was in biology, but, in my heart, I always wanted to be a nurse. A friend of mine, who was head of a science department at a local college, hired me to teach anatomy classes and laboratory experiences. I was offered an opportunity to do something useful and important, when other people might have said, "I can find plenty of people with biology degrees who don't have a handicap." I offset my problem, by making an announcement at the beginning of class. "I am hearing impaired and, therefore, it's your responsibility to get my attention, if I don't hear you." It worked out just fine. The students were great. Their support gave me the confidence to apply to the nursing program and, fortunately, I was accepted.

I didn't ask for any accommodations when I applied to the nursing program. The application asked the question: "Do you have a disability that would affect your ability to complete the program?" I thought I could complete the program. From the beginning, I didn't admit that I had a disability, and I began to take care of things on my own. I made sure that I showed up twenty minutes early for a lecture and waited by the door, particularly the first couple of times, in order to secure my position in the room. I chose a location in the same area of the classroom for each course. It was always in the first one or two rows and always in line to see the lecturer speak. If I made a mistake, I corrected it right away. If there were an overhead projector or other equipment in my way, I would offset that problem by picking a consistent location. After a few weeks, most students tend to sit in the same seat, so I was home free. I never said anything to the professors, but I think one was soon on to me.

I didn't think to ask for anything extra. I'm not a member of the "fairness group." I went to school when everybody was expected to work, and they did. They had to. I felt insecure enough, about having something wrong with me and attempting to enter a profession where I would be expected to function as though normal. I waited a long time for someone to turn around and say, "Why do you want to be a nurse anyway? That is a crazy choice." I never wanted to identify myself as different, not with the other students, and not with the faculty either. But, as I learned later on, I would have to tell the clinical faculty, in the interest of responsible nursing care.

Accommodations

Taping the lectures helped for a while, but, unless I was used to the way the person spoke, it was difficult to hear the tapes, because I had nothing to look at. Excellent attendance, coupled with the proper position in the room, was the only way that worked for me.

A note taker would have helped me, but I didn't want to disclose and ask for help. Every time I was in a situation where the lecture was moving quickly and with a lot of content in a short amount of time, I would lose some of the content because I had to look down to write. It was a big problem, but I never mentioned it. The easiest courses were the ones where the professor handed out the notes in advance. Some professors resist that because they feel they are encouraging students to avoid reading the textbook and doing the necessary preparatory work, to get more from the lecture. Having the notes ahead of time and referring to them while I listened was very important. I can't think of anything that was more helpful. Actually, I would rather have the teacher's notes than a note taker's notes.

Disclosure

When the program called for us to begin our hospital clinical experiences—taking care of patients—I realized that I might have a problem. I went to a faculty member who was coordinating the clinical experience for the first course. I explained to her that I had a hearing loss. She said, "The burden is on you. It's not that you can't do it. The school would never say that we didn't want someone who is handicapped in the program. You were admitted to the program, and we won't hold this against you. But, in order to make sure that you are successful, you need to tell people so that they are aware of it ahead of time." That was the first piece of advice I had in nursing school. Her response made me relax. I soon realized that some of the people I told about my disability would accept it and make adjustments that could make things easier for me; other people wouldn't. Some people can't adjust.

During one of my first clinical experiences in the hospital, I had a professor who was totally intolerant of my situation. The pressure was extreme. However, as I moved along in the program, I found other professors who went out of their way to make sure I could function and do the best job for the patient. If that required talking to other nurses and supervisors and letting them know about my situation, they did what was right for the patient and the hospital. That is important. Even the dean was supportive in her own way, and I felt that if I had her support, I had the program support.

The most negative experience for me was with a professor during a medical-surgical experience in the hospital. From the beginning, her perception was that I wouldn't be able to do my job; therefore, she treated me with that attitude. She never heard me say, "I don't hear you. I need you to speak directly to me."

Most of my problems occurred in clinical courses. My obstetrics clinical experience didn't go well, because we spent a lot of time in a post-conference, at the end of the day. We students were required to share what had happened that day with the group (e.g., "I saw a delivery," or "I was in the nursery."). The instructor also asked us to share how we felt about the experience. The more details shared, the better. I started out with a bad attitude, because I don't like to share my feelings about an experience that quickly. Before I discuss something, I like to reflect on it. That wasn't the way things were to be done, however. As soon as we came off the hospital floor, we had to talk about what had happened. It took me awhile to adjust. I don't mind writing how I felt, because it gave me time to think and put things into perspective.

This particular learning situation wasn't my favorite; I believe it had to do with my hearing loss. I'm not comfortable in a conversational setting, unless I can see everyone speak. I prefer to speak with someone one-on-one. A circular table doesn't work for me. I accepted some of my uncomfortable feelings with these impromptu conferences as being a direct result of my dislike of a scenario where I wasn't in control. I didn't think of it as a hearing impairment problem. Now, I do.

I don't have an amplified stethoscope, although I am considering getting one. They are very expensive. When I was a student, money was tight. I decided I would purchase one only if I couldn't function. When I was evaluated while taking blood pressures in the practice lab, I received a passing grade. Because of this, I didn't see a reason to invest in a special stethoscope.

When we practiced listening to breath sounds, I seemed to hear the same sounds as the other students. I may not hear them identically, but I am able to hear differences between normal and abnormal breath sounds. I can identify if the patient has a problem.

Fortunately, the nurses on the hospital floors didn't tape report on their patients. Therefore, student nurses weren't required to listen to a taped report from the night nurse. That would not have been a positive experience for me. Taped recordings have to be perfect, in order for me to understand them. Many of the hospitals tape report. I was lucky during my training.

Reactions

Like most students, I didn't spend a great deal of time on campus. No one has time, with working, commuting, and going to school full-time. My best friends were the same people who had always been there for me. Family is family. School friendships were related to the course I was taking or to the clinical group I was in. Most of us students completed our clinical day and then left the hospital. There wasn't much socializing.

Most of the students understood that I had a problem and it didn't bother them. They would make slight adjustments to accommodate me. There were a few instances that were not very pleasant, however. For some of our course work we had to work in groups. I was usually picked last to be in a group, like in gym class in grade school. For one project, we had to perform a skit about a patient and family interaction with a doctor and the nurse. The dialog wasn't formatted so I couldn't memorize my lines. I informed my group that I wanted to "play" the doctor, "because she simply stands there and says very little. I am afraid that I won't hear what the other students are saying and I will mess things up for rest of you."

One student turned to me and said, "I don't go along with that, because you can hear anything you want to hear!" I was crushed. This type of thing happened twice with this particular student. The second time, I defended myself and felt better. I had to think about what I wanted to say. I had no response the first time, beyond shock. I hate skits, especially impromptu things, because of my difficulty in participating. I'm very self-conscious then.

Working with patients is the best part of nursing school. They are easier to work with than faculty and other students. Patients were not there to judge or compete with me. Every patient I have ever worked with was happy for my attention. When I tell patients that I am hearing impaired, many of them—particularly the elderly—have the same problem and appreciate my sharing with them. They feel they have met someone who understands their problems. I can't think of a time when a patient had a problem with my nursing care. Patients will deal with anything, if presented the facts with honesty and are shown genuine interest as individuals.

I didn't tell all of my patients about my handicap. Sometimes, as a new nursing student, I got busy with my tasks and didn't speak up when I should have. When I got into a conversation with a patient, though, I always told them about my hearing loss; I couldn't carry on a conversation without them knowing. Often, patients would suspect I had a problem because I have to remove my hearing aids when I use a stethoscope. I still feel real awkward doing this. It's not a pretty move. Sometimes, I remove them before I enter the patient's room. I might say, "I'm hearing impaired. I can't hear properly with the hearing aids inserted when I use the stethoscope." Their understanding usually clears the air for me. Then, I feel free to say, "Excuse me, I can't hear you." or "You'll have to remember to talk a little louder."

The objective for a nursing student with a disability is the same as for a student without a disability. We all want to be successful. The additional burden is on the student, to make whatever adjustments need to be made. The pressure increases in clinical experience classes, such as those taking place in the hospital, clinic, or nursing home. These experiences are, of course, the most important, because that's where we're going to work as a nurse. All students want to do well in their clinical experiences, but, for me, the adjustment was much more difficult. During one of my clinical courses in the hospital, I took a part-time job as a nursing assistant because I was having a hard time with the noise, the various distractions, the many voices, and the new required skills.

Nursing school is stressful, and it definitely took its toll on me over a period of time. The stressful part ran over into other parts of my life. With time, the level of stress does come down.

As I moved along in the student nursing program and learned more about my profession, I came to know that every nurse doesn't have to work in an acute care, hospital setting. Through my course work, I was exposed to a wide range of nursing opportunities in the community—health departments, home care, and clinics. When I realized I had options, I was reassured that I had made the right choice—selecting a major in nursing. Until then, I wasn't always sure. I knew I wasn't comfortable in an acute care hospital setting. The pressure was simply too great.

Recommendations

The first piece of advice I would give any student interested in becoming a nurse is to select a bachelor's degree program rather than an associate degree program, particularly if the student is impaired in any way. The BSN degree will open more doors. Second, I would advise the student to select an area of nursing where he or she can be the most functional and have the best future. It is better for a student with a disability to disclose the disability in school and at work, in order to get the needed support. I wouldn't want anyone to experience what I went through. I was frightened, when I realized I might have lied or made some other serious mistake, even if it was unintentional. It's a difficult decision to make, however. Disclosure is a risk. The individual may not be accepted into the program.

I didn't know much about nursing when I applied to the program. Potential students need to learn more about their career choices. Many will tell you they want to become a nurse, but they have no idea what that entails, particularly the physical and academic demands of being a nurse. Many are accepted into programs without knowing what they are expected to do. Colleges and universities need to do a better job in educating students about career choices prior to admission.

Being a nursing student with a disability, for the most part, is the same as being a nursing student without a disability. There is a lot of stress, but there is for everybody. Most of the students in my program were carrying a full class load and had part-time jobs and family responsibilities. They juggled. Many commuted long distances. What we all had in common was being nursing students. There were more similarities than differences. The differences were small things. Of course, I can only speak about my disability.

One of the most important things to consider when thinking about a career in nursing, is to find out exactly what a nurse does in practice and what is expected of every student in the nursing program. Disclosure of a disability should be made, if it will cause problems. Students with disabilities should ask for the help they need. The training may be difficult at times, but, overall, it can be a beautiful experience that will open many doors of opportunity.

Remarks

Marion wrote about the importance of potential students learning all they can about being a nurse before considering a career in the profession. She recommended a four-year bachelor's degree in nursing, especially for students with disabilities, and suggested that they disclose the disability in order to get needed help and support.

Marion needs to be mindful of the importance of informing all of her patients about her disability. She needs to be proactive in explaining how she uses a stethoscope and the need to remove her hearing aids. A handout of information for patients and families might be helpful.

Learn About Nursing

A student who is interested in a career in nursing should learn as much as possible about a nurse's responsibilities and skills and the different types of nursing programs offered. Nurses are educated in four-year baccalaureate degree programs, two-year associate degree programs, and three-year hospital diploma programs (rare); licensed practical nurses are educated in technical schools and community colleges. Information can be gained from talking to nurses and nursing students, from observing nurses at work, volunteering in a clinic or hospital, spending a day with a nurse, or working a part-time job in a hospital or clinic. Additional information can be obtained from colleges, universities, technical schools, libraries, nursing journals and organizations, and the Internet. High school students should consider joining the future nurses organization at their school or taking a health occupations course and joining a chapter of the Health Occupations Students of America (see Resource section). Gather as much information as possible.

Harassment

A nursing student said to Marion, "You can hear anything you want to hear." This could be considered harassment. Nursing students with disabilities and nursing educators need to be aware that schools, colleges, universities, and other educational institutions have a responsibility to ensure equal educational opportunities for all students, including students with disabilities. This responsibility is based on the Rehabilitation Act of 1973 (Section 504) and the Americans with Disabilities Act of 1990 (Title II), which are enforced by the Office of Civil Rights. Harassing conduct can take many forms, including verbal acts and name calling, nonverbal behavior, such as graphic and written statements, or conduct that is physically threatening, harmful, or humiliating. Disability harassment is a form of discrimination prohibited by Section 504 and Title II, and both provide students with grievance procedures and due process remedies (see Resource section).

Amplified Stethoscopes

An amplified stethoscope may have helped Marion. There are many available, in well-respected brands, styles, and cost categories.

Cardionics, Welch Allyn, Agilent Technologies, and Littmann are companies that make amplified stethoscopes. They can be purchased through local medical supply stores, directly from the company, and via the World Wide Web (see Resource section).

Listening Devices

Auxiliary listening technology may have helped Marion in the classroom. There are a variety of types available, including personal and group FM systems (using radio waves), loop systems (using magnetic waves), infrared systems (using light waves), and hardwire systems (see Resource Section). The devices consist of a transmitter worn by the faculty member and a receiver worn by the student. The system maintains the same voice distance between the lecturer and the student, regardless of the lecturer's movements around the room. Background distortions are also cut down. An education audiologist can specify ways to make the system compatible with the student's hearing aid.

Questions to Ponder

- If Marion had disclosed her disability, would she have been admitted to the nursing program?
- What accommodations might have helped Marion?
- Was patient care compromised due to her disability?
- What accommodations might have improved her ability to provide safe patient care?
- How could Marion have better informed her patients about her disability?

Individualized Nursing Education Program

Marion could have benefited from an Individualized Nursing Education Program. The following program serves as an example of what could have been developed.

Name: Marion
Date:
Disability:

Student has a hearing loss in both ears. According to the student, the higher ranges of sounds are missing completely. She wears hearing aids. She doesn't hear consonants well. Fifty, sixty, fifteen, and sixteen sound much the same.

Current Performance:

Student is a junior in the BSN program, admitted with strong letters of recommendation from previous employers. She has a 3.5 grade point average. Faculty clinical evaluations have been excellent. A letter on file documents her disability.

Impact on Academic Program:

Student's hearing loss may impact clinical nursing courses. Of particular concern are nursing skills requiring an ability to hear, such as listening to blood pressures and heart and lung sounds. Hearing monitors, alarms, patients' calls for help, telephone conversations, and taped reports may also be affected. In lecture courses, student may need front row seating, taped lectures, handouts, a note taker, listening device, CART reporting services or sign language interpreter.

Assessments:

Nursing faculty assessed the student—specifically her ability to hear blood pressures and breath and heart sounds—using tapes of lung/heart sounds and a double-sided stethoscope. Student did not hear heart/lung sounds appropriately. She was able to hear blood pressures, with a regular stethoscope in the campus laboratory. Student states that she can hear and or read lips in lecture courses, if allowed to sit in the front row. She does not use sign language. She would benefit from a note taker.

Technological Devices:

Student would like to try using a listening device in lectures only if other interventions are ineffective. Student agrees to purchase an amplified stethoscope. An amplified telephone may be needed at clinical agencies.

Short-term Goal:

The student will maintain an average grade of C or better at mid-term in all nursing courses. Course work will include examinations, papers, projects, and a demonstration of clinical skills. Clinical courses will include a written evaluation by the faculty member, signed by the student. The student will bring her amplified stethoscope to all clinical experiences.

Annual Goal:

The student will receive a final passing grade (C or better) in all nursing courses. Course work will include examinations, papers, projects, and demonstration of clinical skills. Student will demonstrate ability to use an amplified stethoscope for heart, lung, and blood pressure assessments. Clinical courses will include a written evaluation by the faculty member, signed by the student. Student will meet all university requirements.

Accommodations, Supports, and Related Services

Faculty Advisor Responsibilities
- Refer student to campus Office of Students with Disabilities
- Refer student to campus financial aid office
- Refer student to state vocational rehabilitation to explore eligibility for benefits and possible funding source for amplified stethoscope
- Refer student to vendors for amplified stethoscopes
- Refer student to local deaf services or hearing impaired organization
- Refer student to campus counseling service

Clinical Courses
Objectives related to nursing skills: listening to heart/lung sounds, blood pressures, alarms, monitors, patients' calls for help.

Student's Responsibilities

- Report hearing loss to clinical instructor
- Purchase amplified stethoscope
- Bring amplified stethoscope to all clinical experiences
- Wear pager to all clinical experiences (vibrating)
- Report hearing loss to primary charge nurse on hospital unit or at health care agency
- Arrive early to clinical experiences to get verbal report if report is tape-recorded
- Inform assigned patient(s) regarding hearing loss
- Position all patient monitors in clear view
- Check on assigned patient every 10-15 minutes
- Assess blood pressure with digital blood pressure machine when available
- Use amplified stethoscope for assessments of blood pressure
- Assess patient's heart and lung sounds with amplified stethoscope
- Ask instructor or primary nurse to verify assessments of heart/lung sounds and blood pressure readings when indicated
- Work with assigned student "buddy" if needed
- Schedule time with lab instructor to review and practice use of "99" ("99" refers to an examination technique used to elicit vocal or tactile palpable vibrations through the bronchopulmonary system to the chest wall)

Clinical Instructors and Faculty Responsibilities
for each clinical experience

- Facilitate staff acceptance
- Inform appropriate personnel at clinical agency regarding student's hearing loss
- Facilitate patient acceptance
- Facilitate peer group acceptance
- Provide printed handouts of information presented to clinical group
- Provide ongoing assessments of student's hearing related to clinical skills (blood pressures, heart/lung sounds, monitors, alarms, patients' calls for help)

- Assign student a student "buddy" if needed
- Assess student's need for amplified telephone at clinical site
- Ask all students to speak from front of the room instead of round table discussions during post-conferences

Classroom Instruction
Student Responsibilities
- Meet with faculty member before course begins
- Sit in the front row
- Arrange to tape-record lectures as a back-up to ensure that no information is missed
- Take notes and use note taker notes for comparison only
- Wear receiver for assistive listening device if needed

Faculty Responsibilities for each course
- Allow student to sit in front of the classroom
- Allow student to tape lectures
- Face the class, enunciate well, and speak at a moderate pace
- Avoid standing in front of windows or other light sources
- Provide handouts of material presented
- List new vocabulary or medical terms on the chalkboard or overhead
- Provide announcements, test dates, or changes in schedule on paper, chalkboard or overhead projector
- Wear transmitter for assistive listening device ear if needed
- Provide scripts of movies or videos shown in class if available
- Assign students to small groups by number or draw from a hat

Testing Modifications
None needed at this time.

Office of Students with Disabilities
Provide student with a note taker for fifteen credit hours of course work on the main campus during the fall and spring semesters. Provide student with a listening device, if needed, during the fall and spring semesters.

Transition Needs
An amplified stethoscope will be purchased by the student. No other transition needs have been identified at this time.

Evaluation of Program
The Individualized Nursing Education Program will be re-evaluated at the end of the spring semester or before, if indicated. The student or a faculty member may request a re-evaluation at anytime.

Signatures:
Student_____

Faculty Member (s) _____

Dean or
Director_____

Office of Students with
Disabilities_____

Date_____

CHAPTER 3

FINDING A GOOD PROGRAM FIT
Nursing school with multiple disabilities

Colleen has a back injury resulting from two car accidents. She has limited range of motion in her neck, limited ability to turn and bend, and a weight lifting restriction. At times, she must use a walker or a wheelchair. She has seventy percent hearing loss in her left ear and thirty percent loss in her right ear. Colleen shares her long journey to admission to a BSN program in the South. She is currently working as a nurse and attending graduate school.

The application process to the BSN program was straightforward. I sent the application with a cover letter stating I was a handicapped student and would need admission to the college with a handicapped accommodation—specifically, a weight lifting restriction. On the medical form, I revealed the many surgeries I've had, which would probably scare any normal person to death, but the committee looked at my excellent GPA, and I was accepted on that basis. The assigned advisor asked me to come in for an interview and shocked me by questioning whether I should be there!

I have had two major car accidents. In the first one, I broke my lower back and was paralyzed from the waist down for seven months. After multiple back surgeries to insert rods and remove discs, I went through a rehabilitation program.

In the next car accident, I severely fractured cervical vertebra four (C4), but was saved from being paralyzed from the neck down. I lost functional movement of my legs and had a cervical fusion, involving twenty-seven screws. My jaw was fractured in several places, leaving permanent damage; therefore, I wear an orthotic in my mouth to prevent dislocation of my jaw. I have little range of motion in my neck and no lateral movement.

The injury to my lower back occurred while I was enrolled in a BSN program, the last semester of my senior year. Unfortunately, I wasn't able to continue the program. I had neck surgery because I had lost functional use of my vocal cords. During this ordeal, I became ill with chicken pox, which left me with a significant hearing loss—seventy percent loss in my left ear and thirty percent loss in my right ear.

After the car accident, the nursing school administration terminated my involvement in the BSN program and suggested I become a social worker. Although I probably would have been a good one, it wasn't what I wanted. I didn't think I should settle for something that wouldn't be rewarding for me. I returned to school and received a dual bachelor's degree in computers and business management. With those skills, I believed I could make a living from a wheelchair. After I graduated, I went back to the College of Nursing, but was disappointed once again when their response to my inquiry was, "Why didn't you get a degree in social work?" They didn't say, "We're glad to see you succeeded at something." They didn't have a clue about the difficulties I had worked to overcome.

Disclosure

I applied to hundreds of other nursing programs across the country; I was accepted at only one. In the beginning, I was forthcoming regarding my disability when completing the applications for admission, but, as time went on and I continued to be rejected, I became less open and provided only minimal details. I said I was a disabled student and couldn't lift more than a certain weight. I was never dishonest; it was simply better to wait for a request for details regarding my disabilities.

Rejection came in many ways. Often, I received no response whatsoever from a program, despite my repeated calls. Other programs said their policy required a nursing student to lift x-number of pounds. At a local community college, I was accepted into and completed their Patient Care Assistant Program. Later, I applied for the nursing program offered by the same college. I was told, "There's no way we could consider you as a candidate."

I said, "Why are your restrictions for the nursing program different from those for your Patient Care Assistant Program?" They said,

"They aren't different. You shouldn't have been allowed through the doors of the Patient Care Assistant Program either." I was totally frustrated.

Accommodations

Thankfully, I was accepted into the program I now attend. The university has an Office for Students with Disabilities. They provided a remote control for the doors that are too heavy for me to open. I carry my books in a wheeled suitcase. Sitting however is a problem, as I can't sit for three-hour classes in a regular classroom because of the small desks with inadequate backrests. Most of my teachers understand if I have to stand and walk around at the back of the room. They don't get upset anymore. However, because I can't hear from the back of the room, I limit the time I spend there.

Most of the instructors are aware of my hearing loss. One of them gave me tapes to facilitate the learning of heart sounds. Heart sounds had become a bit of a problem and the tapes helped, because I could literally place the stethoscope onto the tape recorder in order to amplify the sound. I also tape my lectures. Only one professor gave me a hard time about that. He didn't want his lectures taped.

Reactions

When I entered the clinical courses, I needed more accommodations. In the first semester, faculty members were quite concerned about my ability to function appropriately, because I wear a back brace, during clinical coursework. In the initial few weeks, if a patient needed lifting, they assigned another student to work with me until they learned what I could and couldn't do. They seemed to be more concerned about what I couldn't do than what I could do. I can perform many of the procedures expected of all nursing students, but I'm smart enough to know I can't lift a two hundred-pound person without help. Most nurses without a disability shouldn't either. All of the instructors have been agreeable to my getting the assistance I need.

Some of the faculty members have been more wonderful than others. If a situation has required an accommodation for my participation, most have been helpful and come up with a solution. While taking a course that included doing technical skills in the campus laboratory, the beds became a challenge. I had difficulty bending over a bed if it couldn't be raised to a high position. The lab equipment was old and often didn't work, making it hard for me to carry out my duties. I would try, but my limited body mechanics placed me in a precarious position. This situation frustrated one instructor early in the course. Later, we went to the lab with a group of ten students. One of the beds in the lab worked well. Most of my group members said, "This is Colleen's bed." They were good about that. There has been a little resentment with a few of the other students because of the accommodations made for me, but not enough to cause problems.

The faculty members sometimes make accommodations for me without being consciously aware of it. For example, my patient assignments are not always the same as for the other students. The instructors don't give me the most technically difficult patients—certainly not a total care two hundred-pound patient, because they know I can't do every required procedure. Sometimes, they flip out over some of the other things I can do for my patients and ask, "How did you do that?"

One faculty member was particularly wonderful. When my advisor left, she became my advisor by default. During the first couple weeks of school, I went to meet her and said, "This is me. Now you know who I am." We talked about my disabilities and she wasn't at all alarmed.

She said, "Let me know what you need and if there's something we can do to help. We can at least talk about it. Maybe we can't do what should be done, but we can adapt to something that you can handle." She was also receptive to talking with other teachers.

One of my medical-surgical clinical instructors recently had back surgery and wears her back support to clinical experiences. There is an understanding that I know what she is talking about. During a part of this course students must observe in the operating room (OR). I informed her that I wouldn't be able to stand in the OR, and she said, "Fine. If you don't want to be an OR nurse, it doesn't matter." She changed my schedule to exclude both the OR and the recovery room and gave me more medical-surgical experience on the floor. She adapted several things like that in the schedule, and I appreciated it.

Overall, the university administration is still in the dark as to what reality is like for people in wheelchairs. They think if they provide a proper toilet for the disabled student, everything will be fine. There are days when I can't walk without using a walker. I also can't function in clinical experiences on days when I'm in a wheelchair. I can't do my off hospital unit experiences either. I have to blow those days off my schedule. It is impossible to sit during the recovery room clinical experience.

The minute anyone sits in a wheelchair they become a patient because somewhere, in a patient's subconscious, is the notion that a nurse cannot use a wheelchair. During my psychiatric nursing rotation, my legs simply didn't work and I needed to use my wheelchair. The faculty member who taught the course told me I couldn't use it. My brain was still working, so I asked, "Why can't I?" Since we don't give baths or personal care at the psychiatric hospital, and my job was to be with clients in group counseling sessions, I knew I could work from the chair. I quickly saw that the problem was the instructor's and not mine. It was close to mid-term evaluations and her evaluation of me was that I couldn't function. She told this to my entire clinical group of nursing students. I was horrified.

Most nursing students have understood my limitations, but the group that tends to be overly competitive has a difficult time with me. One student, in particular, goes out of her way to comment, if she feels my assignment isn't as difficult as hers. "How dare you think that your problems are worse than mine?" I don't want to be classified as better, worse, or indifferent; I just want my peers to understand that I have a disability that requires some limitations. One day, this student said, "People like you shouldn't bother taking slots in nursing programs from people like us who don't have disabilities." Unfortunately, I have to work with this person every day we have clinical experiences. I want to say, "Hello! I don't think people with attitudes like yours should be nurses either!"

That student is a difficult problem for me, because as tactfully as I try to respond to her comments, it isn't enough. I always seem to be operating from a minority position. I have to learn to have even more tact. I have to constantly be nice and constantly try to please. I'm okay, but I have to show that I'm okay and prove it every day. Nursing is a privilege that I must earn. People like that particular student are really hard to tolerate though.

I expected negative attitudes from the instructors more than I did from the students. After applying to so many nursing programs, I had come to expect negativity from the "upper echelon." I believed that once I got through the door of the program, the students would figure out that I put on my pants the same way they do and we would all be in the same boat. That hasn't been the case with every student. Those who are more naïve, less experienced, and less stuck-up are more adaptive. They are more willing to say I'm okay, or offer to help me. Those who think they are the "cat's meow" are less receptive. That's the cross I have to bear.

Nursing school is tough enough without that stuff. If you don't have your peers' support, it is hard to get your instructors' support, because the students who have a problem with a student with disabilities tend to be the most vocal and whine in the instructors' ears. Last term, I got the backlash from such a situation. My clinical instructor actually told me, "Some of the students are complaining that you're not getting the same experiences they are." Well, whose fault was that? If there was something else I should have been doing, the instructors needed to tell me what it was. If they don't give me the opportunity, I don't have the opportunity to show them I can do the work.

I said to the instructor, "If accommodating me puts you in an uncomfortable position with the other students, then maybe I need to talk to the clinical group." I offered to explain to them what my perception of the assignments was and how we could work out the needed adaptations. She said she didn't think that was necessary. I'm sure it was only one or two whining students complaining to her. I knew that it wasn't an issue among all of the students. That was a frustrating time.

At times I feel isolated from my peers. Perhaps it's self-imposed because of the age gap, or because I am so serious about what I'm doing. I can't abide sitting in a room with students who aren't serious about school. I tried study groups, but being with ten people who don't want to learn is very hard for me. I have to study, and I have to learn the material well. If I don't get my "A," I feel I haven't done my best. Sometimes, I back away from people in my clinical group because they are too immature or not serious enough. I want to get the most from every new experience in order to graduate and pass my nursing boards. I want to be a great nurse.

Once, I went out my way to ask some nursing students to be quiet during class. I was heckled. I finally turned and said to a student, "I swear, for the next class I'm going to buy you a muzzle!"

She said, "Who is going to help you put it on me?"

I was floored. She was my age and not an immature kid. She wouldn't quit. I said, "There are some of us who want to learn. If you don't want to participate, that's fine, but why don't you leave then? Don't make it uncomfortable for the rest of us."

Half of the class applauded and the other half made unacceptable comments. One quarter of the class got up and left. I felt like a jerk, but I'm one of the few people who has the guts to speak up. I paid my tuition, too, and I wanted the opportunity to listen to the lecture. Unfortunately, by taking actions like that I tend to isolate myself. Who wants to hang around with someone like that? At the same time, I single myself out to people who want the same things, and I am able to develop a resource group. I'm not so serious that I don't laugh and joke, too, but not during a lecture. I was brought up in a different era.

On a more positive note, I was nominated to become a member of Sigma Theta Tau, the International Honor Society of Nursing. Only eight students in my class will be inducted, and I was shocked to be one of them. When I received the letter in the mail, I felt honored. It validated everything I was trying to accomplish. It said, "You can do this. You can make it." When I'm a registered nurse, I can say I have belonged to Sigma Theta Tau since my junior year. It doesn't matter that I am disabled.

My experiences with patients have been great. I don't care how difficult the situation, I probably handle most of them better than other students do. After seven months in the hospital as a patient, I have learned a lot about the frustrations of being a patient. I go out of my way to do picky things, like making sure patients have necessary items, like lotion, close at hand, or I find a more comfortable position for them. I have patients who hug me and many who cry with me.

In my last clinical, I had a gentleman who didn't want to go to a hospice to die. He was on continuous morphine to make his pain endurable. I gave him a bath. His girlfriend and his ex-wife were there. I went about my business. We had a good time, and I soon had him in stitches. I made sure he was shaved. He was going to die, but why should his last days be filled with unpleasant experiences? Suddenly, he started to cry. "Nobody has shaved me in four days," he said.

I spoke with his eighty-seven year old father, who also started to cry. "Nobody sees my son as a healthy college athlete anymore. With you taking care of him, I know he will get the best care." We hugged. His brother joined us and we all stood in the hall in tears. His ex-wife joined us and said she had never seen a nurse give better care. That made my day.

I often get patients with huge underlying issues that nobody seems to have caught or taken the time to catch. I talk with them in a way that encourages them to let things out. One heart patient was having unusual feelings after being placed on a new medication. I reported it to the charge nurse. She said that the patient had never complained about it before. Maybe no one had asked her about it. The medication orders were changed. I had made a difference in somebody's care. I don't guarantee that my technical skills are the best in my group, but as far as being a caring person is concerned, I have a great deal to offer. The patients seem to love me. The staff nurses, however, do not.

One patient asked about my back brace. He was afraid that he was going to be too heavy for me. I asked one of the men on the floor to help me. He said, "This little girl can handle this."

The staff nurses are more hesitant. They have a mental boundary that makes them ask, "Are you sure you can do this?" A staff nurse might suggest to my instructor, "I don't think you should give her that patient because the situation may be too difficult for her." I also hear questions about my career choice from staff nurses all the time. "Why the hell do you want to go into this profession? You already don't have a back; you certainly won't have one when you get done with your training!"

Being a nursing student with a disability is challenging! I haven't lost my sense of excitement about everything I get to do. It's wonderful. Like the first time I started an intravenous line (IV), and the first time I put in a Foley catheter. I think those feelings are the same for every nursing student. I probably go home and giggle about it more than anyone else though. I did it! Every little hurdle I scale, the more I believe I can get up and do it again tomorrow. But, tomorrow may be one of those days when my putting two feet on the floor causes excruciating pain. I wonder how I can survive the day, but, somehow, I put one foot in front of the other. The major problem is getting out of bed; but, knowing I'll be giving to someone else helps get me through the aches and pains.

Fortitude has helped me the most. I'm a survivor from way back—a quiet survivor. Now, I'm a little more vocal and more active because I need to be aggressive about getting from point A to B. I can't do it as easily as I could before. It's by the grace of God and a lot of prayer that I get out of bed each day. The first hour of every morning, I wonder why my body has to go through so much pain. People at school don't know that it may take me two or more hours to get ready in the morning. Other students can be ready in twenty minutes. It also takes me three hours to drive to school. I have to be willing to lose all of my friends and to isolate myself socially. I say to friends, "I still love you dearly, but now that I'm a nursing student, I only have twenty minutes to talk to you." I've become more disciplined.

The only outside supports I have are my mom and dad. My dad was a rural doctor in the Midwest. He instilled in his children that if we were going to do something, we should do it right. We grew up with challenges, and sitting in our room and moping wasn't allowed. Failing at something was not an option. Our family was secure, with a strong religious background and faith in God. I always knew that the Man upstairs had something He wanted me to do. Our faith made us stronger people. I can't say I haven't had moments when I've thought quitting was a better option than dealing with my disabilities and pain; but, those were simply bad days and I got past them.

I've had the good fortune to have people in my life at the right time, when I was at the end of my rope. I treasure those people who have come into my life for even a short while. It is hard for me to accept help. I spend so much time challenging myself that I tend to lose the reality that it's okay to let someone help me. I don't have a problem doing for someone else, but having them do it for me is hard. I have one really good girlfriend who says, "Shut up. I'm doing it."

I keep thinking that I have something to offer. If more nurses were cognizant of what it's like to be on the other side of the bed, they would be better nurses. In one nursing class, an instructor asked how many students had been a hospital patient. It was amazing. Only four of us had ever had surgery. We have an advantage in knowing what care we wanted and didn't receive from the nursing staff, and what we appreciated.

Recommendations

The most important thing I would share with students with a disability who want to become a nurse is that they must be willing to face and deal with the challenges, and to put aside everybody's negative comments. I'd tell them, "You can do it, but it has to be something you want so badly that you'll give up everything and everybody in your entire life to accomplish the goal."

Going to school is a full-time job. I'd advise them not to work, unless it was absolutely necessary. They should explore every opportunity for scholarships and financial aid, instead. In addition, they should adapt their schedules accordingly, getting pre-requisite courses out of the way before beginning the nursing program. They should plan on attending summer school, for instance.

When applying to different schools, they should look carefully at the program's philosophy. If the program emphasizes technical skills and competitiveness, they may be looking at a program that won't take a serious look at their participation.

I'd tell them about the importance of studying the laws that protect students with disabilities, such as the ADA and the Rehabilitation Act, and to be aware of the accommodations they are entitled to receive. They should know their assets and what they do best and write about every wonderful thing they believe about themselves, and send that positive message to the schools, rather than focusing on what they can't do. In their very first meeting with an administrative member, I would advise them to back away from negativism. If they are being given barricades, sometimes it is better to see if there's another way that doesn't have as many. If the system is one with many barricades and they want to proceed anyway, they should take them one step at a time. No matter what they do, they should not try to take on the whole damn system at one time. They should take one step at a time.

Some programs may put students with disabilities on probation and give them a chance to prove themselves. They should take the opportunity. In my first BSN program, I offered to sign medical waivers, after a lot of attorney's fees and battling. At that point, I decided there were too many barricades. I was emotionally drained after seven months in the hospital, and needed about two years of rehabilitation and rest before I could take on the challenge of a school system. Students with disabilities have to be able to take rejection, emotionally, because they'll take a lot of it before they get what they want. They can't stop though. They have to hang on until they find the right program.

Remarks

Colleen stresses the need to find the right nursing program and to look carefully at the program's philosophy and expectations. She recommends that students focus on their assets and be prepared for rejection. She advises against working while attending nursing school, and suggests that students explore all other sources of financial aid, instead, and pace their schedules according to their needs. She also advises students with disabilities to be aware of the laws that protect them against prejudice.

Legal Issues

Information about the laws that protect students with disabilities (the ADA and the Rehabilitation Act of 1973 [Section 504]) can be obtained on the Internet, from local legal aid societies, advocacy groups, or any form of university library (see Resource section).

Harassment

Some of the comments nursing students made to Colleen could be considered harassment. Nursing students with disabilities and nursing educators need to be aware that schools, colleges, universities, and other educational institutions have a responsibility to ensure equal educational opportunities for all students, including those with disabilities. This responsibility is required by the aforementioned legal doctrines and legislative acts passed by Congress. Harassing conduct may take many forms, including verbal acts and name calling, as well as nonverbal behavior, such as graphic and written statements, or conduct that is physically threatening, harmful, or humiliating. Disability harassment is a form of discrimination prohibited by Section 504 and

Title II, both of which provide students with grievance procedures and due process remedies (see Resource section).

Financial Aid

Nursing students with disabilities should explore all possible sources of financial aid. Numerous scholarship and loan opportunities exist within the public and private sectors. Students also need to investigate possible Social Security benefits or their eligibility for state vocational rehabilitation programs (see Resource section).

Amplified Stethoscopes

Colleen did not disclose whether or not she used a hearing aid or amplified stethoscope. Her hearing loss indicates that she might benefit from using an amplified stethoscope. There are many choices available. Cardionics, Welch Allyn, Agilent Technologies, and Littmann make special stethoscopes, which can be purchased through local medical supply/home health care stores, direct from the company, and via the World Wide Web (see Resource section).

Listening Devices

Auxiliary listening technology may have helped Colleen in the classroom. There are a variety of types available. Some consist of a transmitter, worn by the professor, and a receiver, worn by the student. A listening device would have allowed Colleen to stand at the back of the classroom when she was unable to sit, and still hear the lecture. Information about listening devices can be obtained on the World Wide Web (see Resource section).

Wheeled Suitcase for Books

Colleen used a wheeled suitcase (e.g., the type used by flight attendants) to tote her books to classes. Most students with back problems would benefit from using a similarly convenient apparatus to transport books, instead of a backpack or briefcase. They can be purchased at most department stores.

Back Supports

Colleen wore a back support for all clinical experiences. A physician should recommend the specific type to be worn, depending on the location and severity of the individual's back injury. Back supports can be purchased from home health care and medical supply stores, as well as on the Internet.

Questions to Ponder
- What accommodations might have helped Colleen?
- Was patient safety compromised due to her disabilities?
- What accommodations would have improved her ability to provide safe patient care?
- What measures could have been taken to facilitate better peer acceptance?

Individualized Nursing Education Program
If Colleen had fully disclosed her disabilities, an individualized nursing education program would have been useful to both her and the nursing program in general. The following plan serves as an example of what might have been developed.

Name: Colleen
Date:
Disability:
This nursing student has a back injury resulting from two car accidents. She has a limited range of motion in her neck, a limited ability to turn and bend, and a weight lifting restriction. At times, she must use a walker or a wheelchair. In addition, she has a seventy percent hearing loss in her left ear and a thirty percent loss in her right ear, secondary to chicken pox.

Current Performance:
Colleen is a junior in the BSN program. In a previous program, she completed all course work, except for the last semester. She has a bachelor's degree in computers and business management, and she completed a patient care assistant program at a community college. Her GPA is 3.9. She has excellent letters of recommendation. A letter from her physician is on file.

Impact on Academic Program:

Colleen's back injury, limited range of motion, and weight lifting restriction may impact clinical nursing courses, particularly objectives/nursing skills related to lifting or bathing patients, making beds, and performing cardio-pulmonary resuscitation (CPR). Her hearing loss may impact clinical nursing courses, particularly objectives related to nursing skills (e.g., listening to blood pressures, heart sounds, auscultation of lungs, hearing monitors, alarms, patients' calls for help, telephones, and taped reports). At various times, she may need to use a walker or wheelchair in clinical settings. Her back injury and hearing loss may impact lecture courses. Helpful accommodations include front row seating, handouts, a note taker, permission to stand during lectures and to tape them, and a listening device. The Office for Students with Disabilities may need to provide a remote control door opener, more accessible classrooms, a note taker, a listening device, and a tutor.

Assessments:

Nursing faculty assessed the student. Assessments included evaluation of the student's ability to lift patients, make beds, perform cardio-pulmonary resuscitation (CPR), and, also, of her range of body movement. Student will have difficulty moving and bathing heavy patients in bed, and performing cardio-pulmonary resuscitation (CPR). She will be further limited during days she uses a walker or wheelchair.

The student's hearing was evaluated, specifically her ability to hear blood pressures and breath and heart sounds, using tapes of heart/lung sounds and a double-sided stethoscope. Student did not hear heart/lung sounds appropriately and was unable to hear blood pressures with a regular stethoscope. A special stethoscope will be needed. Student states that she can hear material presented in lecture courses, and does not need a note taker or listening device at this time.

Technological Devices:

Student agrees to purchase an amplified stethoscope. At present, she denies the need for classroom supports, such as a note taker or listening device. She will need access to a computer and software programs that provide opportunities for simulation of nursing skills.

Short-term Goal:

The student will maintain an average grade of C or better at mid-term, in all nursing courses. Course work will include examinations, papers, projects, and demonstrations of clinical skills. The nursing student will bring a special stethoscope to all clinical experiences. Clinical courses will include a written evaluation by the faculty member, signed by the student.

Annual Goal:

The student will receive a final passing grade of C or better in all nursing courses. Course work will include examinations, papers, projects, and demonstrations of clinical skills. The nursing student will demonstrate the ability to perform heart, lung and blood pressure assessments with an amplified stethoscope. Clinical courses will include a written evaluation by the faculty member, signed by the student. Make-up work, due to illness or hospitalization, will be completed by the end of Summer Term "A." Student will meet all university requirements.

Accommodations, Support, and Related Services

Faculty Advisor Responsibilities

- Refer student to campus Office of Students with Disabilities
- Refer student to campus financial aid office
- Refer student to state vocational rehabilitation, to explore eligibility for benefits and possible funding source for amplified stethoscope
- Refer student to vendors for amplified stethoscopes
- Refer student to local deaf services or hearing impaired organization

Clinical Courses

Objectives related to nursing skills: listening to heart and lung sounds, blood pressures, alarms, monitors, patients' calls for help; bathing, lifting, turning and ambulating patients, performing CPR, treatments, medications.

Student's Responsibilities related to hearing loss

- Report hearing loss to clinical instructor before clinical experience begins
- Purchase amplified stethoscope
- Bring amplified stethoscope to all clinical experiences
- Report hearing loss to primary/charge nurse on unit of hospital or health care agency
- Request verbal report on assigned patient, if report is taped (may need to arrive early)
- Position all patient monitors in clear view
- Inform assigned patients of hearing loss
- Check on assigned patient every 10-15 minutes, or more often, if needed
- Assess blood pressures with amplified stethoscope and digital blood pressure machine Ask instructor or primary nurse to verify student assessments of heart and lung sounds on patients
- Schedule time with lab instructor to review and practice use of "99," when assessing patient's lungs
- Work with assigned student "buddy" if needed

Student's Responsibilities related to back injury

- Schedule appointment with lab instructor to review and practice body mechanics
- Report back injury and occasional need to use walker/wheelchair to clinical instructor before clinical experience begins
- Wear back support/brace, per physician's order, to all clinical experiences
- Use wheeled suitcase to transport books
- Report back injury and weight lifting limit to primary or charge nurse
- Work with assigned student "buddy" when turning patients,

bathing patients, making beds, providing treatments and passing medications
- Collaborate with primary/charge nurse regarding development of a plan of action if CPR is performed
- Demonstrate knowledge of nursing skills using various methods (e.g., hands-on, verbal, written, diagrams, computer programs)
- Make up missed clinical days in established timeframe

Clinical Instructors and Faculty Responsibilities
for each clinical experience
- Provide handouts of information presented to clinical group
- Inform hospital/clinic charge nurse and appropriate personnel about student's hearing loss, back injury, weight lifting restriction, and possible use of walker or wheelchair
- Collaborate with staff members and student regarding a plan of action if CPR is needed
- Assign student a "buddy" to work with (lifting, bathing, turning patients, treatments, medications)
- Provide student with diverse opportunities to demonstrate nursing skills (e.g., hands-on, verbal, written, diagrams, computer programs)
- Arrange for alternate clinical experiences and make-up clinical experiences when needed (e.g., absence due to illness, need to use walker or wheelchair)
- Establish a mutually agreed upon system of communication between a faculty member and the student
- Facilitate student-patient, student-staff, and student-peer group acceptance
- Provide ongoing assessments of student's hearing related to clinical skills (blood pressures, heart and lung sounds, monitors, alarms, patients' calls for help)
- Assess student's need for amplified telephone on hospital floors or home care agency

Classroom Instruction

Student's Responsibilities

- Meet with professor before course begins
- Sit in the front row
- Stand at the back of the room when necessary
- Attend all classes or make arrangements for lecture to be taped
- Wear receiver for listening device if needed
- Make up missed course work within established timeframe

Faculty Responsibilities

- Allow student to sit at the front of the classroom
- Allow student to tape lectures
- Allow student to stand during lectures
- Provide handouts of presented material
- Enunciate words carefully and talk at a moderate pace
- Face the class and use audiovisual aids
- Provide scripts of films and videos when available
- List new vocabulary or medical terms on the chalkboard or overhead
- Provide announcements, test dates, or changes in schedule on paper, chalkboard, or overhead
- Wear transmitter for listening device if needed

Testing Modifications

Student may need time extensions, make-up examinations, adjustable-height table, and permission to stand during an examination. Computers and software will be available in the campus nursing laboratory.

Office of Students with Disabilities

The Office of Students with Disabilities will provide the student with the following supports:

- A note taker, if needed, for fifteen credit hours of course work on the main campus during the fall and spring semesters and six hours of course work on the main campus for Summer

Session A.

- A listening device, if needed, for fifteen credit hours of course work on the main campus, during the fall and spring semesters, and six hours of course work on the main campus for Summer Session A.
- A remote control for doors that are not automatic.
- A tutor if needed.

Transition Needs

An amplified stethoscope will be purchased by the student. When taking the NCLEX, the student may need time extensions, permission to stand when needed, and an adjustable-height table. Information regarding requests for NCLEX accommodations has been given to the student. Employment counseling is recommended.

Evaluation of the Program

This Individualized Nursing Education Program will be re-evaluated at the end of the fall semester or before, if indicated. The student or a faculty member may request a re-evaluation at any time.

Signatures:

Student_____

Faculty Member (s) _____

Dean or
Director_____

Office of Students with
Disabilities_____

Date_____

CHAPTER 4

DISCLOSING IS IMPERATIVE
Nursing School with Crohn's disease

Sylvia has Crohn's disease, a stress-related bowel disease that causes diarrhea, weight loss, nausea, fatigue, pain, and abdominal cramps. She is on a special diet and medication. Sylvia shares her path through a BSN program in the South. She graduated and is working as a nurse.

In 1975, I was diagnosed with Crohn's disease, which is an inflammatory bowel disease that attacks different areas of the intestine. At first, the doctors thought I had colitis, which is more or less contained to one area of the colon, but then they saw that I had more involvement of my colon and small intestine. Basically, Crohn's disease involves diarrhea, abdominal pain, nausea, weight loss, and fatigue. Researchers don't know what causes the disease or how to cure it. They do know that it is stress related and that most people who have it are overachievers.

Crohn's disease can usually be managed with diet and medication. If untreated, the inflammation can kill the cells lining the colon, leading to ulcers, bleeding, abscesses and severe abdominal cramps. In some people, complications include intestinal obstruction, fistula formation, and intestinal perforation. Prednisone is an anti-inflammatory drug that helps, but it has terrible side effects when taken for a long period of time. Long-term use of steroids causes as many problems as it alleviates. Overall, this disease can take a great emotional toll on people; it often causes isolation and embarrassment.

Disclosure

When I applied to the university, I included a letter "To Whom It May Concern" at the university, and not to the College of Nursing. The letter explained my disability. I believe there was a section in the application that asked the question, "Do you have any medical disabilities?" Since I'm on Social Security disability, I thought an explanation of my disability was important to include; I hoped to receive a grant or whatever financial aid might be available for me. After a wait that seemed like forever, I received my letter of acceptance into the BSN program.

My experience in the nursing program has shown me that strength has as much to do with coping, so I try to take life one day at a time. A primary problem with Crohn's disease is diarrhea. If it's not managed properly, it keeps me confined to the house. This can present a problem when I'm sitting in a classroom lecture or participating in a clinical experience, such as working with patients in the hospital setting.

My special diet can present another challenge, especially if I depend on cafeteria food at school or at the hospital. I usually take food from home. I juice a lot of my food, which includes fresh fruits and vegetables, like carrots, cabbage, grapes and apples. It's very hard to fit my required diet into a long day at school or work.

While I was in nursing school, I was hospitalized a few times. I had a bowel obstruction and needed surgery. At certain times, I've tried to ignore the fever, pain and other symptoms because of a final examination or due-date of a paper. Waiting too long to get to the hospital has sometimes put my health and life in danger.

During my junior year in the BSN program, I started to confide in my professors about my disability, and to more fully explain why I had to be excused from class and why I walked in and out of the classroom so often. I finally realized that if a professor didn't know why I kept moving in the classroom, it could be very disruptive to the lecture. It could also give the wrong impression about me. I didn't want a professor to think that I was bored or that I left class to make a phone call. Crohn's disease is a serious condition and I would only leave a lecture if it was absolutely necessary. The professors were, ultimately, more understanding when they knew I had a problem.

Last summer, my illness spontaneously worsened. In retrospect,

I should have given my clinical teachers a letter from my physician stating that my disease, coupled with fatigue and stress, may cause me to miss some clinical days. Perhaps I should have had such a letter in my file, too.

Memories of one particular experience will stay with me for a long time. I was scheduled to be the team leader for my group of students at the hospital. This meant I was to be at the hospital earlier than they. I was responsible for reviewing the nursing students' patient assignments, checking changes in patients' medical orders, discharges, and other important information, to share with the group members when they arrived. I awoke at 2:30 a.m. with diarrhea and what I thought was a flu bug. I didn't think to call into the hospital and leave a message that I might be out sick. I'm an overachiever and I thought I could make it in if I pushed myself. I loved working in the hospital and we had little clinical experience as it was. The alarm rang at 5:30 a.m. and I must have shut it off, but I don't remember. I awoke at noon in total shock and disbelief. I went to the doctor that afternoon and received a note to give to my professor. I called her to apologize as soon as I returned to my home. For those who might not be aware, not calling in or showing up for a clinical at the hospital is a real no-no when you are in nursing school.

At the end of the semester, I met with my professor for my evaluation. She said, "You are going to be a fabulous nurse and I would love to give you an "A" because you have certainly earned it, but you missed a clinical day and you didn't call the hospital or me." She went on to say, "I have to lower your grade because you were irresponsible." I accepted her decision, but from that point on, I gave my professors a note from my doctor stating my medical condition and informing them that, if there were ever absences, they should take my medical condition into consideration.

Fatigue is a major problem with Crohn's disease. Many times, I didn't think I had the energy to get out of bed. If I was running a fever and had classes, clinical experiences at the hospital, or laboratory experiences, it was particularly difficult to drum up the needed energy. Of course, there were endless chapters to read and papers to write, and all of these activities took their toll. I hated getting up in the morning. I never got enough rest. When the alarm sounded, I often felt it would kill me to get up, but as soon as I was dressed, my attitude would change. I'd go right through the day without stopping. Even after class was over, I didn't rush home.

Diarrhea hasn't been a major problem for me. It's a symptom I can control until I get a break. It's almost like having a "nurse's bladder." If I have to give two more medications and need to visit the bathroom, I hang in there. That's how it is with me. Even though I have a disability, I don't stop what I'm doing to take care of myself; rather, I take care of everyone else first. The nursing faculty has been supportive throughout the program. As I shared before, I respected and accepted that my grade was lowered because I didn't call in sick. It was irresponsible on my part not to remember that rule, when people were depending on me. I would have received an "A" if I had done things the proper way. If I were in the professor's shoes, I would have done the same thing.

I've learned not to stress over my grades. The difference between an A and a B+ doesn't bother me as much anymore, because I realize it's not a reflection of my capabilities as a nurse. I'm still an "A" nurse, and I know that. When I first started in the program, I was obsessed with my grade point average. One of my professors was wonderful and helped me put grades in the proper perspective. She had a calm and soothing spirit that transferred to everyone around her. This was great for someone like me, who is stressed most of the time.

Reactions

I love working with patients the most. One of my professors told us to encourage patients to talk about themselves and their situations, and about how they feel about their illness. Essentially, the focus should be on getting the patients to talk, not ourselves.

Whenever I had patients with diverticulitis, colitis, or Crohn's disease, I shared that I knew what they were going through, because I have the same problem and have had the same surgery. I disclose my situation, but I am careful not to share too much. I don't want the patients to focus on me instead of themselves.

Occasionally, other nursing students were a problem. There was one female student who had a straight "A" average. She made a few comments about my missing several clinical days. During a psychiatric nursing clinical experience, I missed quite a few days. I called in each time and the professor was wonderful, being fully aware that I had Crohn's disease. For every clinical day that I missed, I wrote a report or research paper for her. The professor and I communicated well and we had a great understanding.

A couple of the other students didn't appreciate the fact that I missed several clinical days and still got an "A" in the course. One didn't say anything to my face, but I knew she talked about other people and made their business her business. She and another student were in a study group for another class and I heard her talking about everyone else. I knew she would talk about me to other students. She commented that she had made a mistake when she wanted to take off a clinical day. She called the professor and said, "My husband wants to take me to New York City for my birthday, so I'm going to miss clinical tomorrow." The professor said, "That's unacceptable. I'm happy it's your birthday and your husband wants to take you to the city. I would like to go on a little vacation too, but I can't." The student responded, "Some of us can take a day off and be honest about it. I was in a clinical with a nursing student who missed half the semester." I was sitting near her when she related this conversation, so I knew she was referring to me.

I'm pretty much a loner, so faculty support was very important. Another instructor was like a mentor to me. When she discovered I had Crohn's disease, she said, "Oh, my God, I can't believe it. Don't you worry. Take care of yourself. I'll take care of things for you here." She was unbelievably supportive. She said, "You are a good nurse. If you miss a class or clinical day, it's okay." Her attitude helped me accept getting a "B+" instead of an "A."

I don't talk to my friends or family about my disorder. They ask me how I feel now and again, but it's not a big issue. My sister isn't supportive about anything I do, because she and I have a sister conflict that has been going on for many years. Her attitude is "Let's see if you can finish this!" Where she gets that, I don't know, because I worked in my previous career for many years. When I made the decision to go into nursing, she viewed me as being unstable. I viewed it as being courageous enough to make a career change in the middle of my life in order to do something I really wanted to do, rather than continuing to do something merely because I was trained in that field. My brothers live far away and are very distant. My parents are supportive of my decision to go into nursing, but I wish I had more encouragement from my siblings.

When I was first diagnosed, I went to a support group for people with Crohn's disease. We met after work and talked about how things were going and what medications worked or didn't work. Bonding with others who have similar problems helped me cope. I related to each group member and that was important to my acceptance of the disease.

Recommendations

I would stress to nursing students with a disability that it is important to take their situation calmly and to not fear disclosure. It's okay. The more up front they are with the faculty, the better. Let it be known that they may lack energy. List some of the characteristics associated with the particular disability. The students should inform the instructors about their strengths and how they can compensate for their disability, too. They should focus on those strengths and not get discouraged. They should share honestly with other people. There are many caring people in the nursing profession, so one should not ever get discouraged.

It's very stressful to be a student nurse, even without a disability, as the demands can be great. Overall, it can be a positive experience because nursing is such a challenging and exciting profession. Many things are taxing for those of us with a disability, but the more tests we face, the greater the sense of achievement when we reach our goal.

Remarks

Sylvia shares the need to be up front and honest with faculty. An informed professor is more likely to understand the situation and to make accommodations. Sylvia suggests that a nursing student with a disability get a letter from his or her physician that explains the disability and its possible ongoing symptoms. The letter can be placed in the student's file and given to the professors.

Questions to Ponder

- What accommodations might have helped Sylvia?
- What accommodations might have improved her ability to provide safe patient care?
- Was patient care compromised due to her disability?
- What interventions could have facilitated better understanding from her fellow nursing students?

Individualized Nursing Education Program

An individualized nursing education program would have been helpful for Sylvia and the faculty members. A program for Sylvia might have looked like the following example.

Name: Sylvia
Date:
Disability:
Student has Crohn's disease, an inflammatory stress-related bowel disease that causes diarrhea, weight loss, nausea, fatigue, pain, and abdominal cramps. Complications can result, including the development of bleeding, ulcers, abscesses, and fistulas. Student is on a special diet and medication as needed.

Current Performance:
Student is a junior in the BSN program. She has excellent letters of recommendations and a 3.8 grade point average. Student has been absent from classes, due to illness and surgery. A letter from her physician will be attached, when received.

Impact on Academic Program:
Student's medical condition may continue to result in frequent absences from lectures and clinical experiences. Plans need to be developed for her to make up missed work (e.g., extension on due dates for assignments, make-up examinations, taped lectures, make-up clinical days). Her condition requires that she be able to leave classroom lectures when needed. During clinical experiences, she needs the opportunity to use the bathroom.

Assessments:
Student will provide the nursing program with a letter from her physician that outlines her medical condition.

Technological Devices:
No needs for special devices have been identified.

Short-term Goal:
The student will maintain an average grade of C or better at mid-term, in all nursing courses. Course work will include examinations, papers, projects, and demonstrations of clinical skills. Missed course work, examinations, and clinical time will be completed, during or before the university's winter break. Clinical courses will include a written evaluation by the faculty member, signed by the student.

Annual Goal:
The student will receive a final passing grade (C or better), in all nursing courses. Course work will include examinations, papers, projects, and demonstration of clinical skills. Missed course work, examinations, and clinical time will be completed by the end of the summer session. Clinical courses will include a written evaluation by the faculty member, signed by the student. Student will meet all university requirements.

Accommodations, Supports, and Related Services
Faculty Advisor Responsibilities
- Refer student to Office for Students with Disabilities
- Refer student to financial aid office
- Refer student to the university counseling service
- Refer student to local Crohn's Disease support group
- Inform student about student health services
- Advise student to get a letter from her physician

Clinical Courses

Objectives related to patient care and demonstration of nursing skills.

Student's Responsibilities

- Notify clinical instructor about medical condition
- Inform primary or charge nurse about medical condition
- Collaborate with instructor and primary nurse to establish break and lunch times
- Work with assigned nursing student "buddy" (cover breaks)
- Bring food to clinical experiences
- Organize patient care and pace activities
- Report absences to hospital or instructor at designated time
- Report signs/symptoms of illness to clinical instructor ASAP
- Seek appropriate medical care when needed
- Collaborate with instructor to develop plans for make-up clinical days
- Make up clinical days within established time frame

Clinical Instructor and Faculty Responsibilities for each course

- Inform primary/charge nurse about student's special needs
- Assign student a nursing student "buddy" to cover breaks
- Collaborate with student to establish break and lunch times
- Arrange for make-up clinical experiences following student absences

Classroom Instruction

Student Responsibilities

- Provide faculty member with a letter from physician
- Attend classes as regularly as possible
- Make arrangements to have lecture taped when absent
- Call faculty member ASAP if class or examination will be missed, or paper will be late
- Collaborate with faculty to make up work that is missed
- Complete make-up examinations, papers, projects, or other course work in established time frame

Faculty Responsibilities for each course
- Allow student to leave lecture when needed
- Allow student to tape record lectures when absent
- Allow student to have time extension on paper or project submission date when needed
- Arrange for make-up examination when needed

Testing Modifications
Make-up examinations may be needed

Office of Students with Disabilities
No services needed at this time

Transition Needs
No transition needs have been identified at this time

Evaluation of Program
This Individualized Nursing Education Program will be re-evaluated at the end of the spring semester, or before, if indicated. The student or a faculty member may request a re-evaluation at anytime.

Signatures:
Student_____

Faculty Member (s) _____

Dean or
Director_____

Office of Students with
Disabilities_____

Date_____

CHAPTER 5

CONQUERING FEAR
Nursing school with deafness

Rhoda has a fifty percent hearing loss in both ears (bilateral), caused by hereditary neural damage. She graduated from an AD program in the Midwest and went on to get a BSN. She describes her experiences in nursing school and working as a nurse. Her fear of disclosure remains constant.

About ten years ago, I received an AD from nursing program at a community college. Before I attended the AD program, I received a bachelor's degree in business. Don't get me wrong; I always wanted to be a nurse. I wanted to attend a nursing program from the beginning, but being honest about my disability backfired on me.

I applied for the AD nursing program and visited with the director of the program, where I admitted I had a problem with my hearing. The director told me she didn't think I could make it through the program. I was more than a little discouraged, but continued to apply to the general college. Later, I was accepted and received a bachelor's degree in business. Soon after graduation, I reapplied for the nursing program and, this time, didn't disclose my hearing problem. The same director of nursing was there; I kept my fingers crossed and hoped she wouldn't remember me. My grade point average was pretty high and I hoped it would tell a lot about my abilities. Thankfully, I was accepted into the program.

I have an approximate fifty percent hearing loss in both ears (bilateral). Neural damage has run in my family for many years. The only time I wear a hearing aid is to work and school. Since I do a lot of driving, I wear the hearing aid in my right ear to allow me to hear someone riding in the passenger seat. Although I got my first hearing aid when I was sixteen, I never wore it. I hated it! It was uncomfortable. I was amazed later, when I heard birds chirping. I never knew they made a noise. And, I was amazed at how much noise water makes. Despite knowing the hearing aid would allow me to hear such things, I still did not wear it. I know some sign language, but I rarely use it.

When I was a junior in my business program, I transferred to a big state university. I was concerned about my hearing because the classrooms were so much larger than at the community college. That's when I decided I would wear a hearing aid … but only one. At the time of my fitting, I was told I wouldn't be able to tolerate the noise that would come in from wearing two hearing aids. I have seen other specialists who thought I could wear two, but as long as I'm comfortable with one, I don't see why I should wear two. I don't want to become dependent on wearing them.

Reactions

When I was in nursing school, one of my instructors caught on that I had a hearing problem. She went to the director of the nursing program and said, "I think she has a problem." The faculty members didn't find out from me, only through their assumptions. I discovered they knew about it, but I wasn't directly confronted. One of the other nursing instructors let me know what was said in the meetings and warned me to be careful.

The director didn't want me in the nursing program, and we clashed over a number of issues. Several times she said to me, "Your degree in business isn't going to help you here." I think she was intimidated that I came into the program with a degree, since most of the other students didn't have one. When she learned I had a hearing loss, she thought this was the way to get me out. By the time I graduated, she had dropped the class from thirty to ten students. It was very important to her to have a 98–100 percent pass rate on the nursing board examination. We all knew about it.

It's interesting that the instructor who shared what was discussed in the faculty meetings didn't help me when I had her as an instructor for a clinical course at the hospital. In fact, if she wanted to talk to me or needed me to do something, she relied on my hearing her from the end of the hall. Another student would say, "The instructor wants to talk to you." The instructor didn't accommodate my hearing loss in any way, although she knew I couldn't hear her. It didn't make sense. When she realized my roommate was helping me, she tried to trip me up. She assigned my roommate to a patient at one end of the hall and me to a patient in another hall. She knew that I couldn't get my roommate to help me and would be left stranded. She couldn't stop us from taking breaks and lunch together, though, and we could share information then.

When we took blood pressures, I know the instructors expected that I wouldn't be able to hear, but I did fine. There were no problems because the sound went straight into my ear from the patient. I even heard the blood pressure fine when the instructor used the double tubing stethoscope, which allows two people to listen at the same time. They couldn't get me on that, but I felt like they really wanted to see me fail.

In the beginning, I did have problems distinguishing lung sounds. The instructors didn't pick up on that because they didn't check on what I said I heard. Lung sounds change so quickly that it would be hard to say that I didn't hear the sounds correctly. They could have tricked me if they had used a tape. I wouldn't have been able to distinguish the lung sounds. Since I've been in practice as a nurse I've been able to fine-tune that skill. Let's face it, there are nurses who have been in practice for years and still can't distinguish lung sounds appropriately.

Throughout the program, I only had problems with the director and with one instructor. The director was not verbally negative about my hearing, but her attitude was decidedly negative toward me as a person. I always felt she was waiting for me to slip up. I didn't give her an opportunity to see me slip up because the instructor I mentioned earlier usually alerted me. Overall, the instructors were great. Since it was a small school, I had some of the same instructors for several courses. For example, the obstetrics instructor also taught pediatrics, and the psychiatric instructor also taught medical-surgical nursing. I never had a problem with them because my grades were good. It's hard to find fault with a student who makes good grades. I received the same patient assignments as the other students and they were always fair.

The night nurses usually recorded report for the day nurses. When we arrived on the nursing unit, the students were supposed to listen to the taped report. That was a challenge for me because some of the taping was of poor quality. I got around this situation by arriving early enough to receive a verbal report on the patient I would care for that day.

Our program was small to begin with and got smaller every semester, due to students dropping out. Most students commuted long distances, so relationships were hard to develop outside of class. I lived with two other nursing students who had some medical background: one worked for a doctor, and one was an emergency medical technician (EMT) before coming into the program. The one who worked for a doctor quickly caught on that I had a hearing problem and she was very accommodating and enunciated well. After class she would basically know what I had or had not heard. We pulled each other through the program. I had better study skills than both of my roommates, and they had the practical experience and listening skills I lacked. I pulled them through with bookwork knowledge and emotional support, and they pulled me through by listening for me. If I said I hadn't heard something, they would tell me what I had missed, depending on who was around. It's not that the other students didn't help out; we weren't friends per se, because we lived so far away and didn't see each other outside of class.

I never explained my disability to patients. I was too afraid they would report it and say, "She's not a very good nurse." I feared they could use that one thing to discredit my nursing care and me. Patients have said, "You didn't hear that?" or "You walked out of the room. I called your name and you didn't hear me." Patients have also said little things that made me aware they picked up on my hearing loss, but I never verified what they said. I simply didn't respond to their comments. I would say I was on the way out, or I had my mind on something else, but I never confirmed that I didn't hear them. I usually didn't hear a request when my back was turned or when I was on my way out of the door. Although I always wore my hearing aid, I wear my hair down so that the aid is covered. While practicing as a nurse after graduation, I have had patients notice my hearing aid and make rude comments like, "Can't you hear?" or "What's the matter?"

Getting through nursing school as a student with a disability can be very stressful. I work harder to get my grades than other students do.

Sometimes, I want someone to say, "You know, she deserves an extra brownie point, because she goes through a lot to get a grade." I have to read everything. I can't skim the chapters. When I sit in class, I can't doodle or daydream. I have to pay strict attention. But I can't tell anyone about my struggles. They would probably say that I should be doing the work anyway.

As a person with a disability, I compete with myself, not necessarily with the other students. I have to prove to myself that I can do it and that I am "normal." Even though it is important for everyone to get an "A," it is even more so for me. I want it because I need to prove that, despite my disability, I can do it. Nursing school was very stressful and it took a toll on my health. I developed an ulcer. It got better after graduation, but returned when I returned to school to get my bachelor's degree in nursing.

Disclosure

My biggest fear was that somebody would find out I had a disability and say, "I'm sorry, but we have to cut you from the program." It is a fear you can't imagine. I had no doubt that I would be ousted if found out. I know I should have told my instructors in the beginning, but I didn't. My lack of disclosure was like lying. I don't believe in lying, but I did it. I was constantly worried about when the bomb would drop. If it were to drop, I feared I would have to start all over again, perhaps in a different field altogether.

Having a disability made me feel isolated from others. When I started nursing school, I didn't know anyone. For the first two or three months, I struggled to make friends. I wanted to make sure I chose my friends wisely. I didn't want friends who would "rat me out" the minute they got mad at me.

Determination got me through the nursing program. My challenge was the knowledge I had been told I couldn't do it. I had never enjoyed much self-esteem. Nobody encouraged me in high school. Who wants to encourage somebody who can't hear? I graduated with a 3.9 grade point average when I earned my bachelor's in business. Then, I finally realized I could do the work in nursing school if no one found out about my disability.

My family was as supportive as they could be. We have had hearing problems on my mom's side of the family for generations so my disability was nothing new. They don't consider deafness a situation that needs moral support. You live with it. You deal with it. Life goes on. It's not that there is no support from them; it's simply no big deal.

My mom and dad didn't support me much at all. When I was a child, I never felt they were overly protective because hearing loss was such a natural occurrence in my family. When I was a young child, I got good grades in school. Every school year, the teachers had a seating arrangement. One of them wanted to move my seat to the back of the room. The next day, my mother went to her, explained the situation, and made sure she put me at the front of the room. Most teachers would say, "She does so well."

My mother would say, "Yes, she does well because she can hear at the front of the room!" Sometimes, my mother and the teachers argued over the seating arrangements, but that's really the only thing my mother did for me in school. At home my hearing was treated as normal.

My husband at that time was supportive, but not in a gung-ho way. He was there, and he never doubted that I could do it. I remember him saying, "You got your bachelor's in business, so you can do this, too. There is no big difference. You'll make it. But, you don't have to do all this studying." My studying was the biggest issue with my husband. He would always say, "I don't know why you study so much. You're going to get an A. You get A's all the time." What he didn't understand was that I got my A's because I studied so hard.

Religion wasn't a big deal in my family. We used to go to church a few times, but years ago I started going to a Baptist church on a regular basis. Now, I have a personal relationship with God. It's not something that I talk about, though. I make it sound like a joke, but I'm very serious when I say, "God sat beside me and helped guide my hand into the right answers." I believe He has helped me more than anybody will ever know. People who don't know me would find that hard to believe because my relationship with God is so personal. It's been a great help for me to know that He is behind me.

Recommendations

If I were in a position to advise other students with a hearing loss, I would stress the need for making arrangements with the Office for Students with Disabilities early, even before classes begin. I would suggest that they ask for a note taker (particularly in a review class before an exam), because taking notes in class is very difficult when compensating for a hearing loss. It would be helpful if a note taker were in every class. I'm not saying the students shouldn't take their own notes. The note taker's notes should be used for comparison purposes only, but sometimes one word can make a big difference. If the Office of Students with Disabilities agrees to keep the situation confidential, I would ask for a note taker to be sent into all the classes. The best case scenario would be for the note taker to be so inconspicuous that nobody, not even the professor, knows for whom the notes are being taken. In that way, the student with a disability could be accommodated, without being seen as "special" in the eyes of the other students or professor. If the situation is kept private, a sense of normalcy is maintained for the student, while allowing the student to maintain pride and dignity.

Finding a buddy is also critical. If a student is attending the program without existing friends, perhaps the campus Office of Students with Disabilities could facilitate linking the student with other students with disabilities. Peer support is an enormous help, especially in nursing school. My roommate depended on my emotional support, and I depended on her ears. Without each other, we may have both thrown in the towel.

Disclosure of a disability is a major decision that can only be made by the individual student. There can be benefits as well as risks, but, if students can get by without disclosing, I would advise them to keep quiet. They may need more help, but disclosure will mean they may get less respect. The other students may not be accommodating and the teachers may treat them differently. There is a trade-off between getting help and maintaining pride and dignity.

Being a nursing student with a disability is a more stressful and fearful experience than it is for normal students. The bonus is the experience is filled with more pride upon finishing the program.

After graduation, I was hired by a nearby hospital for a position on a medical-surgical nursing floor. The staff knew I graduated second in my class, which was a factor in my being hired. The next challenge was the Nursing Board Examination, which I took about three months after graduation. I passed the examination with flying colors.

About six months later, my husband and I moved to another state and I got a job in an ICU. I enjoyed working in an ICU because I didn't have to worry about the other nurses learning about my disability or about hearing patient call bells. In an ICU, the nursing care is one-to-one—one nurse, one patient. This unit was small, so I often worked alone. If I needed help, a licensed practical nurse (LPN) was assigned to me. Working alone wasn't stressful for me; in fact, I like to work alone.

After about six months, though, I got bored and took a position at a heart institute in the area. The work was very exciting and I learned a lot, but answering the telephone to receive orders from doctors became a major problem. I'm not good with telephones because they are usually not made for people with a hearing loss. After about six months, I quit.

Now I'm working in another ICU and doing fine, except for the telephones. At the last two hospitals, the staff nurses figured out that I have a hearing problem. A supervisor approached me and said she wanted to give me a hearing test. I was very offended because I didn't want the hospital to know the extent of my hearing loss. If they found out how bad my hearing was, I would probably have been out of a job. I told the supervisor that I didn't think it was necessary, and she agreed not to test me.

One of the nurses I work with said something to me about my hearing, but I fluffed it off. I won't give anyone at work a definite answer to questions about my hearing. I usually say, "Why do you ask? Do you have a problem with my nursing care?" I'm honest about the situation with my friends, but not with anyone at work. I'm always afraid to tell another nurse- afraid that if, he or she gets mad at me about something, I will be reported and lose my job.

Most of the doctors at the hospital are foreigners and are difficult to understand, making communication a challenge. When I don't understand them, they become very impatient and get the information from someone else. One doctor said, "Look me in the face! Now do you understand?" This infuriated me. I find that the foreign doctors tend to be the rudest.

When I was interviewed by the director of a home health agency, she said, "I hear you have a problem with your hearing." I asked her how she found out, and she told me that a nurse who works at the agency told her before I was interviewed.

I resented that another nurse let the news out before I had a chance to. I said, "Yes, I have a problem with my hearing." I had to admit it. The director asked, "How do you deal with that?" and I told her that when I listen with my stethoscope, I listen better than other nurses do. I don't deflate a blood pressure cuff so quickly that I can't catch a number. I deflate the cuff slowly, like I'm supposed to, and listen longer than other nurses because I know I need to catch it.

A couple of years ago I applied and was accepted into a BSN program. I was bored again and wanted a BSN degree to go into community or home health nursing. All of my experience had been in ICUs, and I worried about what I would do when I am older and could not work the floor because my hearing had worsened. If I couldn't work the floor, there was no reason I couldn't do paperwork. I knew the BSN program would include experiences in home and community nursing. I was concerned that I wouldn't get everything I needed to know from the lectures, so I applied for a per diem position in home health and was hired by a local home health care agency. The director was a real sweetheart. I don't think she would have hired me if she didn't feel I could do the job. I asked her if she could get me a telephone designed for the hearing impaired, because in home health care I have to call my patients before I make a visit. The director said she would work on it. The agency has only called me to work a couple of times so far.

Throughout my course work in the BSN program, I have always tried to get personal work experience as a supplement to what we would learn in class. At the hospital, I worked on developing relationships with the nurse managers prior to taking the management course. It's hard to find a place to do your management project if you're not working in a hospital and aware of the ins and outs. The same goes for my efforts to get home health experience prior to the home health nursing course.

The BSN program is going well, though the note taking is still the hardest part. The professors' voices are primarily female. Women speak very softly and are difficult to hear. I wish I could sit in the front of the class and not wear my hearing aid. It's a shame that I have to wear it. Recently, one professor got very frustrated with me. She had to repeat something two or three times for me. She knows I have a problem because we have discussed it.

Accommodations

Class handouts are great. I love professors who provide class handouts and lecture by the handout. One professor uses them all the time, so it's no shock that I love her class. Another professor occasionally looks at me and makes sure I get the information. I appreciate that from her. It's an accommodation without making a big deal about it. If a professor knows she has a hearing-impaired student, she should stand at the front, at a focal point, where the student can read her lips. I had one professor who walked to the back of the classroom for his lecturing. After class one day, I approached him and said, "I'm having a problem hearing you." I did "come out" that time, which really surprised me.

I went home and said to my husband, "I don't know if I messed up or not. I told this professor he had to stand in the front of the classroom because I couldn't hear him when he walked in the back. This is the first time I have made a disclosure."

I'm getting braver, but I'm over forty years old now. I ought to be braver!

Remarks

Rhoda focuses on the risks of disclosure because of her need to maintain pride and dignity. She does not disclose her disability to instructors, nurses, or patients. Rhoda needs to improve her understanding of the importance and responsibility of disclosure. She ignored comments made by patients that should have been addressed. She needs to learn from comments made by patients and be proactive in explaining her situation. A handout for patients and families that introduces herself might be helpful.

Rhoda also suggests that nursing students with disabilities choose friends wisely and develop a buddy relationship for emotional support. She recommends an unobtrusive note taker for a nursing student with a hearing loss and suggests that nursing professors provide students with handouts, lecture from the front of the room, and look at a student who has a hearing loss when they are aware of the disability.

Amplified Stethoscopes

An amplified stethoscope would have been helpful to Rhoda. There are many choices available for people with a hearing loss. Special stethoscopes are made by companies such as Cardionics, Welch Allyn, Agilent Technologies and Littmann. They can be purchased through local medical supply stores, directly from the company, and via the World Wide Web (see Resource section). Cardionics also manufactures a software program for a Pocket Monitor that provides a visual display of heart and lung sounds on a personal digital assistant (PDA).

Listening Devices

Auxiliary listening technology would have helped Rhoda hear classroom lectures. A variety of types consist of a transmitter, worn by the professor, and a receiver, worn by the student. The listening device helps to maintain the same voice distance between the lecturer and the student, regardless of the lecturer's movements around the room. Background distortions are greatly reduced. Information about listening devices can be obtained on the World Wide Web (see Resource section).

See-Through Masks

The ability to lip read is important for many people with hearing loss. The opportunity to lip read can be compromised when medical professionals are wearing masks, such as in the operating room or during a procedure. See-through masks are being developed and should be available in the near future (see Resource Section).

CART Reporting

CART reporting could assist a nursing student or nurse with a hearing loss. CART reporting services provide captioned realtime text in various settings such as classrooms, meetings and seminars.

Questions to Ponder

- If Rhoda had disclosed her hearing loss, would she have been admitted to the nursing program?
- How should Rhoda have answered questions from supervisors and colleagues about her hearing loss?
- How could Rhoda have informed patients and staff about her hearing loss?
- Was patient care compromised due to her hearing loss?
- What accommodations might have helped Rhoda?
- What accommodations might have improved her ability to provide safe nursing care?
- What technology could have assisted Rhoda?

Individualized Nursing Education Program

If Rhoda had disclosed her disability during her associate degree program, an individualized nursing education program might have looked like the following:

Name: Rhoda
Date:
Disability:
Nursing student has a fifty percent hearing loss in both ears (bilateral), caused by hereditary neural damage.

Current Performance:

Student is a freshman in the Associate Degree Nursing Program. She has a bachelor's degree in business. She graduated with a 3.9 grade point average and has excellent letters of recommendation. A letter from her physician is on file.

Impact on Academic Program:

Student's hearing loss may impact clinical nursing courses. Of particular concern are nursing skills requiring an ability to hear, such as listening to blood pressures and heart and lung sounds. Hearing monitors, alarms, patients' calls for help, telephone conversations, and taped reports may also be affected. In lecture courses, the student may need front row seating, taped lectures, handouts, a note taker, CART reporting services, a sign language interpreter, or a listening device. The Office of Students with Disabilities may need to provide a note taker, a listening device, a sign language interpreter, CART reporting service and a tutor.

Assessments:

Nursing faculty assessed the student. The student's hearing, relevant to patient care, was evaluated, specifically her ability to hear blood pressures, and breath and heart sounds. Tapes of lung/heart sounds were used and a double-sided stethoscope. The student did not hear heart/lung sounds appropriately. She was able to hear blood pressures with a regular stethoscope in the campus laboratory. Student states that she would benefit from a note taker for lecture courses. She is not interested in using a listening device at this time. The student knows sign language, but declines a sign language interpreter. A tutor is not needed.

Technological Devices:

The student agrees to purchase an amplified stethoscope and consider use of a Pocket Monitor. An amplified telephone may be needed at clinical agencies. The student prefers to use the services of a note taker, rather than a listening device, or CART reporting service in lecture courses.

Short-term Goal:

The student will maintain a grade of Pass, at mid-term, in all clinical nursing courses, and a grade of C or better, in all nursing theory courses. Course work will include examinations, papers, projects, and demonstrations of clinical skills. The student will bring a special stethoscope to all clinical experiences. Clinical courses will include a written evaluation by the faculty member, signed by the student.

Annual Goal:

The student will receive a final grade of Pass in all clinical nursing courses and a final grade of C or better, in all nursing theory courses. Course work will include examinations, papers, projects, and demonstrations of clinical skills. Student will demonstrate the ability to use an amplified stethoscope for heart, lung, and blood pressure assessments. Clinical courses will include a written evaluation by the faculty member, signed by the student. Student will meet all additional college requirements.

Accommodations, Supports, and Related Services

Faculty Advisor Responsibilities
- Refer student to campus Office of Students with Disabilities
- Refer student to vocational rehabilitation to explore eligibility for benefits and possible funding sources for amplified stethoscope
- Refer student to vendors for amplified stethoscope
- Refer student to local deaf services or hearing impaired organization
- Refer student to campus counseling service

Clinical Courses
Objectives related to nursing skills: listening to heart sounds, breath sounds, blood pressures, alarms, monitors, patients' calls for help.

Student's Responsibilities
- Report hearing loss to clinical instructor before clinical experience begins
- Purchase amplified stethoscope
- Take amplified stethoscope to all clinical experiences
- If report is taped, get to clinical early to receive the report in person
- Report hearing loss to primary/charge nurse on unit of hospital or health care agency
- Inform assigned patient(s) regarding hearing loss
- Position all patient monitors in clear view
- Check on assigned patient every 10-15 minutes
- Assess blood pressure with stethoscope and digital blood pressure machine

- Assess blood pressure with amplified stethoscope if needed
- Assess heart and lung sounds with amplified stethoscope
- Ask instructor or primary nurse to verify assessments of heart and lung sounds on patients
- Work with assigned student "buddy" when needed
- Schedule time with lab instructor to review and practice use of "99" when assessing lung sounds

Clinical Instructor and Faculty Responsibilities

- Inform hospital/clinic charge nurse and appropriate personnel regarding student's hearing loss
- Provide handouts of information presented to clinical group
- Provide ongoing assessments of student's hearing related to clinical skills (blood pressures, heart and lung sounds, monitors, alarms, patients' calls for help)
- Assess student's need for amplified telephone on hospital floors or home care agency
- Facilitate staff, patient and peer group acceptance
- Assign student a student "buddy" when needed
- In post conferences, ask all students to speak from front of the room, instead of a round table discussion

Classroom Instruction

Student Responsibilities

- Meet with professor before course begins
- Sit in the front row
- Attend all classes or make arrangements for lecture to be taped
- Take notes and use note-takers' notes for comparison only
- Wear receiver for listening device if needed

Faculty Responsibilities

- Allow student to sit in the front of the classroom
- Allow student to tape lectures
- Provide handouts of presented material
- Face the class, enunciate words carefully, and talk at a moderate

pace
- Avoid standing in front of windows or other light sources
- List new vocabulary or medical terms on the chalkboard or overhead
- Provide scripts of films and videotapes if available
- Provide announcements, test dates, or changes in schedule on paper, chalkboard, or overhead
- Wear transmitter for a listening device if needed

Testing Modifications
None needed at this time

Office of Students with Disabilities
The Office of Students with Disabilities will provide the student with the following supports:
- A note taker for 15 credit hours of course work on the main campus during the fall and spring semesters
- A listening device if needed, on the main campus during the fall and spring semesters
- A tutor if needed
- A referral to the "Buddy Program" to link student to other students with disabilities

Transition Needs
An amplified stethoscope will be purchased by the student. No other transition needs have been identified at this time.

Evaluation of the Program
This INEP will be re-evaluated at the end of the fall semester, or before, if indicated. The student or a faculty member may request a re-evaluation at anytime.

Signatures:

Student_____

Faculty Member (s) _____

Dean or
Director_____

Office of Students with
Disabilities_____

Date_____

CHAPTER 6

Sharing with Patients
Nursing school with diabetes

Monica is a nursing student who has diabetes. She attended a BSN program in the South. The challenge of being on medication and the need to eat snacks and lunch at regularly scheduled times during clinical experiences is stressed. Monica is currently working as a nurse.

A few years ago I was diagnosed with diabetes. Initially, I was able to control it with exercise, diet, and weight control. When I started a family, it became increasingly more difficult to keep my blood sugar under control. My doctor put me on medication. Part of my daily regimen is to continue exercising at least three times a week and to eat snacks two hours after meals at specific times of the day. Surprisingly, I seem to have more reactions than I had before I began the medication. Even after I exercise, I usually carry juice or something to eat in order to prevent a reaction.

When I applied to the nursing program at a four-year institution, I didn't disclose my diabetes. I attended classes and always brought a snack with me, such as milk, juice or even coffee. I was afraid to say anything because I didn't want to be singled out from the other students. I took care of things on my own without any accommodations.

During my clinical experiences, I was happy to learn that the hospital units kept plenty of milk, crackers, and other snacks on hand for the patients. The selection was even better in pediatric units. I told myself, "Okay, I can handle things at the hospital as well." I used the patient snacks whenever I needed them.

Disclosure

During one of my clinical experiences at the hospital, I was finally forced to tell people about my disability. It was about ten o'clock in the morning, and I had missed my snack because we were busy with patients. I was setting up an intravenous infusion (IV) and the professor was standing beside me. Because I was already stressed out, I became very confused and thought I might pass out. As I was making rounds on my patients, I told my professor that I needed a glass of milk because I felt I was about to have a low blood sugar attack. I forced myself to say, "I have diabetes."

Fortunately, the professor said, "Sure, go get it."

After that incident, I mentioned my situation to another clinical instructor. She didn't have a problem with it either. She simply wanted to be assured that I had a snack with me. Once I opened up about my situation, I noticed that other people understood. I was much better off when people were aware of my situation. I stopped putting myself in potentially dangerous situations. I felt more secure knowing I could respond to my body's warning signals.

Reactions

When I told other students about my disability, some did treat me differently. Some handled it well and others didn't. In certain situations, some students tried to overprotect me, an act which made me uncomfortable. They would say, "Can I get you something?" or "Did you see what time it is? Have you had a snack?" After a while, I was concerned they thought I was someone special.

Sharing my disability with patients, however, has been a great help to me. After I disclose my situation, they seem more comfortable with me and more confident about my abilities. When I discuss diabetes, I appear self-assured because I speak from experience. Particularly with diabetic patients, I can say, "Look at me. I'm fine. I'm in nursing school, I have three children, and I manage to live with the disease. You can do this, too. Everything is going to be all right." None of my patients have been negative or have said, "I don't want her to take care of me because she has a disability."

I've only gained increased respect and self-confidence from sharing my situation with patients. I have a positive attitude, and I try to stay in shape. Seeing is believing for most of us. I could talk until I was blue in the face, but seeing me at work tells a more effective story. I see myself as a role model for anyone trying to work in the world and cope with diabetes at the same time.

Working in the hospital has helped me deal with my disability. People are people, whether they are students or patients. That helps me keep things in perspective. Diabetes is not as bad as other disabilities I have seen.

My family has been very supportive. They know how important the nursing program is to me. They offer to help in different ways, especially when it comes to watching my children. We try to keep the holidays a special family time. I'm Jewish and my husband is Catholic, so we celebrate Christmas and Hanukkah. Neither one of us attends church or synagogue regularly, but we have tried to teach our children to believe in God.

Last semester was a very difficult one for me. I tried to do too much and took up some bad habits. I started smoking again after having quit years ago. The stress of being in nursing school was too much and my diabetes was out of control. Stress affects my diabetes more than not eating. It got so intense one time, that I considered making an appointment to see a university counselor. I didn't because my schedule was too busy, but somehow, I got through the semester. When I finished my final examinations, I started to exercise more and got my life back on a decent schedule. I wish I could have told the faculty more about my needs without drawing undue attention to myself. I would have been much better off if I could have told them more.

The long and short of the story is that a student nurse with a disability feels different, and that feeling is hard to deal with. I have found that working with patients is not as scary as the nursing school experience per se. In the hospital, I felt I could relate to the patients and to their health problems better than a nursing student who hasn't had an illness. Having a chronic illness is a way of life that necessitates doing what has to be done. In that respect, my disability has helped me through the nursing program.

Recommendations

My advice to other nursing students with disabilities would be to tell people about their disability. They shouldn't be afraid. It's not worth keeping the secret and not getting needed help. I suffered and my family suffered, because I was not able to take care of myself the way I should have because of my fear of disclosure to faculty members.

I wish there was a stronger support system for students with disabilities. It's easy for me to say these things now, but to actually do them is difficult. We need to bring up these matters in a way that encourages students to go to each other. Many students with problems are afraid to talk about them with others. In some instances, an illness can get worse due to the stress in a nursing program. Some students are afraid to reveal this because their peers may make them feel it's an excuse for not doing a good job. Also, they fear they'll be forced out of the program. There have been times when I've worked a shift at the hospital, from eight in the morning to ten in the evening, without a break. Students are supposed to go, go, and when they are tired, go even longer still. That's the way it is, so understandably, I was afraid to say anything about my fatigue for fear I'd be dismissed from the program.

A student nurse with a disability has more difficulties than other students. Emotional and physical stamina are tested with greater intensity. There is constant concern that the stress will worsen the symptoms, and, ultimately, it usually does. In the end, though, I believe the experience can be even more rewarding than it is for other students, especially when you graduate.

Remarks

Monica emphasizes how important it is for a nursing student with a disability to share information about the disability with faculty members, because disclosure assists the student in obtaining the needed supports and promotes the student's ability to take better care of his or her health. She discusses the importance of faculty support and an environment that promotes disclosure.

Monica also underscores the need for students with diabetes to carry snacks to classes and clinical experiences, to take regularly scheduled breaks and meals, and to maintain a habitual exercise regimen to assist with weight control and stress reduction.

Monica suggests that the nursing school should reach out to students with disabilities through the use of university counselors, who may offer helpful suggestions for coping and provide other emotional support. Monica shares her positive experiences working with patients and discusses how patients helped her gain confidence.

NOTE: Food on hospital floors is intended for use by the patients and not by nursing students.

Questions to Ponder

- If Monica had disclosed her disability, would she have been admitted to the nursing program?
- What could Monica have done to make the experience more positive?
- What accommodations could have helped Monica?
- What accommodations could have improved her ability to provide safe patient care?
- How could faculty members make the environment more open to a student's disclosure of a disability?

Individualized Nursing Education Program

If Monica had fully disclosed her disability, an individualized nursing education program might have looked like the following example.

Name: Monica
Date:
Disability:
Student has diabetes. She is on medication and needs to eat snacks and lunch at regularly scheduled times. Letter from physician is on file.

Current Performance:

Student is a senior in the BSN program. She has a 3.4 grade point average. Faculty clinical evaluations of the student have been above average.

Impact on Academic Program:

Fluctuations in blood sugar levels from diabetes can result in hypoglycemia (mental confusion, dizziness, weakness, pallor, tachycardia, diaphoresis, fatigue, headache, blurred vision seizures, coma) and hyperglycemia (acetone breath, dehydration, weak and rapid pulse, Kussmaul's respirations). Student's condition may impact her ability to provide nursing care to patients. Student needs to carry snacks with her to all classes and clinical experiences.

Assessments:

Nursing faculty assessed the student. The student reported that her blood sugar was in good control most of the time. She needs to eat regularly scheduled snacks and lunch. Stress has a negative effect on control of her diabetes.

Technological Devices:

No technological devices are needed.

Short-term Goal:

The student will maintain an average grade of C or better at midterm in all nursing courses. Course work will include examinations, papers, projects, and demonstrations of clinical skills. Student will take snacks to all clinical experiences during fall semester. Student will obtain a Medic Alert bracelet. Clinical courses will include a written evaluation by the faculty member, signed by the student.

Annual Goal:

The student will receive a final passing grade of C or better in all nursing courses. Course work will include examinations, papers, projects, and demonstrations of clinical skills. Student will take snacks and wear a Medic Alert bracelet to clinical experiences throughout the academic year. Clinical courses will include a written evaluation by the faculty member, signed by the student. Student will meet all university requirements.

Accommodations, Supports, and Related Services

Faculty Advisor Responsibilities
- Refer student to the Office of Students with Disabilities
- Refer student to the university counseling service
- Refer student to an area diabetes association
- Refer student to the campus financial aid office, if indicated
- Advise student to get a letter from her physician.

Clinical Courses
Objectives related to providing nursing care to patients in clinical situations.

Student's Responsibilities
- Take medication ordered by physician
- Report medical condition to clinical instructor at the beginning of the semester
- Carry snacks to all clinical experiences
- Wear Medic Alert bracelet
- Inform primary or charge nurse of disability
- Work with assigned student "buddy"
- Schedule/coordinate breaks and meals with instructor, primary nurse, and student "buddy"
- Organize patient care; pace activities
- Convey any signs and symptoms of hyper/hypoglycemia to instructor or primary nurse immediately
- Seek counseling, if needed
- Schedule exercise and stress-reducing activities

Clinical Instructors and Faculty Responsibilities
- Inform charge nurse and appropriate hospital or health care agency personnel of student's disability
- Schedule student to work with a student "buddy"
- Plan the student's breaks and meal schedule according to student's health care needs
- Request permission for the student to eat a snack from patient

provisions in an emergency situation

Classroom Instruction

Student Responsibilities
- Inform professor about disability
- Carry snacks to class

Faculty Responsibilities
- Allow student to eat snacks during classroom lectures

Testing Modifications
- Student may need to eat a snack during an examination

Office of Students with Disabilities
University policy prohibits eating in the classrooms. An allowance will be made for the student to eat in classrooms.

Transition Needs
No transition needs have been identified at this time.

Evaluation of Program
This Individualized Nursing Education Program will be re-evaluated at the end of the fall semester or before it indicated. The student or a faculty member may request a re-evaluation at anytime.

Signatures:

Student_____

Faculty Member (s) _____

Dean or
Director_____

Office of Students with
Disabilities_____

Date_____

CHAPTER 7

QUESTIONING YOUR ABILITIES
Nursing school with a wheelchair

Christine is a nurse who sustained a spinal cord injury while in nursing school in a middle Atlantic state. She is a T-4 paraplegic and uses a wheelchair. She shares her experiences as a BSN and master's degree student, as well as her employment experiences.

In December of my junior year of nursing school and during the last week of the second semester, I was in a car accident. The girl driving the car was also a nursing student. She returned to school with a broken arm and leg and on crutches.

The car accident left me as a T-four paraplegic. I was in the hospital when final examinations were given for that semester. The professors passed me on the basis of my grades before the accident. With only one semester left to complete my junior year, I had finished my medical-surgical nursing course and was enrolled in pediatric nursing. In order to complete the requirements of the BSN program, I needed to complete clinical courses in community and home health nursing.

I was on a ventilator for about a month. No surgery was performed on my back because I was in critical condition. After the first month, I had to wear a body vest for about six months. I wasn't allowed to participate in rehabilitation until the body vest was removed, so I couldn't do lifts or transfers. I couldn't even turn myself because my fracture wasn't stabilized, and my mother did everything for me. I couldn't even catheterize myself because of the body vest. I remained in rehabilitation for about a month. I was taught various self-help procedures over a four month period.

After leaving the hospital, I continued with outpatient rehabilitation. The staff at the spinal cord center was surprised at how much I knew about my disability. The occupational therapist said, "We want you to do a transfer now. Try to get your pants on and off."

I said, "I can't. My doctor told me that I shouldn't do a transfer yet. I can't use my arms in that fashion. Dressing skills require a lot of lifting."

The therapist didn't seem to understand the extent of my injury; she was constantly saying, "You're a T-four paraplegic. This is what you should be able to do." I said, "I'm a T-four paraplegic with an unstable fracture. I don't care what you tell me to do, I am not doing it. I'm going to do what my orthopedic surgeon says I should do for two more months." I called my doctor and he called the therapist and told her the same thing. I left the therapy center and never went back.

By the time my vest was removed, I was aware that many of the therapists were not very knowledgeable, and if they were, they weren't putting the whole picture together. I taught myself to do almost everything. My thirteen-year-old brother taught me how to put my wheelchair in and out of my car. He sat in the car and took the chair apart and we talked it out. I said, "That's a good way! That's how I'll do it!" I put my chair in the car a different way than most. I teach others and my patients how to do it my way now. That's some of what I've done in the last few years. I teach patients different ways to do the same activity.

I got out of the hospital in April and took an elective course in the summer at a local college. In the fall, I took two more courses at the same college. I returned to my nursing school one year later to complete my last semester. That's when I drove for the first time.

Reactions

The administrators and faculty were involved with me right from the beginning, and they were very positive and accommodating. When they heard from my friends that I had said, "I'm not coming back," they actually came into the hospital and said, "You are coming back." I was still matriculated and working on some course work. I could have finished with my undergraduate degree in psychology without returning to the school, but decided nursing was what I wanted.

Both of my parents were very worried about me. The dean of the nursing school told my mom that she would look out for me. I'm glad I didn't know it then, I would have been paranoid. The three of them did a lot to help me.

My school was small and very old. The campus was not very accessible. There was a ramp on the first floor that went up two stories. The doors were wide enough to get into one particular classroom and bathroom so, consequently, that classroom was the only one I used. The school made an accommodation for me by putting my classes in that room, and they had clearly thought it out.

The school also gave me a parking spot. Nobody was allowed to drive onto the campus. Students and personnel had to walk from the parking lot to all of the buildings on campus. I was allowed to drive up to the building. Security knew when I was having classes. I could call security at any time to unlock the gates, but they always had the gates unlocked when I arrived, and they left them open until I left campus. They also had clickers for the doors I needed to use. People would constantly say, "Christine, why are you here? There are no people in wheelchairs here." I was evidently the first wheelchair student.

The only accommodation the school didn't provide was housing. At that time, none of the dormitories were accessible for students using wheelchairs. Fortunately, a friend was the basketball coach, and his wife had been my hospital roommate when I was injured. She helped me find a place off campus. Although it was not wheelchair accessible, the building's owner constructed a ramp for me. We called my apartment "the dungeon", because the ramp went down, down, down into the dark building.

My family and friends were incredible. My dad has called me every single morning since the day I was injured. He asks me, "What classes do you have? What's going on? How's the weather?" This has gone on for years now. I was dating a guy who came to visit me every weekend and every Wednesday. I suspect he had a little pact with my parents.

The semester I returned to nursing school, I took a clinical course in community health nursing. I was worried about it because the instructors could send students all over the county to see patients. Fortunately, my instructor set it up so that all of my patients lived in rural communities and had ramps on their houses.

One of my patients had a pretty serious heart condition and used a wheelchair. He was a high level quadriplegic. The guy was about six feet, two inches tall. His wife was only about five feet tall. I taught her how to do his turning, catheterizing, and the rest of his home program. I believe I was good for them, and they were certainly good for me. They were very helpful, and my self-esteem got a boost... a positive experience.

I made my home visits with another nursing student because I had a car and she didn't. In my nursing program, the faculty always paired students. I didn't know the other student prior to this clinical course, although she knew who I was.

Because I lost a year of school, I graduated with a class of students that I didn't know. My best friends had already graduated and left the area. Most of my friends were older than I was, even though we started the nursing program together. The students were nice and fairly positive, but they were not my friends. I didn't hang out with them; they had their own things going on and I didn't try to move in. I was going through a lot, physically and emotionally, and I wasn't looking for them to be my friends. I wanted to get in and get out of the school. That was my mission.

The other nursing students weren't interested in my disability, except for the one student who did her community health experience with me. She learned so much about spinal injuries from me that she's probably an expert today. We drove hundreds and hundreds of miles in a rural area. I'd have to say to her, "I'm sorry you have to get out of the car because I have to catheterize myself." She really learned a lot!

Many of my patients were surprised when I showed up at their house. The quadriplegic man knew I was going to be in a wheelchair, but most of my patients didn't appear to know and they were usually shocked. "Oh, my gosh. She's in a wheelchair!" some would say. Patients and their family members still say this, and they immediately question my ability as though my having a physical disability has affected my mind. Every nurse's ability should be questioned, especially in a rural area when a medication is being administered; however, a nurse wearing a nice little white dress and walking briskly into the house will probably not have her ability questioned as much as I would have mine questioned. My being in a wheelchair seems to project to people that I'm not as smart as someone who doesn't use a wheelchair. If I were a smart nurse, in other words, I wouldn't be in a wheelchair! I don't know why, but people do have preconceived ideas about disabilities.

Once I break down the first barrier, people are more comfortable. I learned this after I was injured, but I got another lesson with patients in that rural setting. I was the only nurse the patients would have. I had their medications and I was required to take their blood pressure and check on their narcotics use, and that was that.

We don't know what other people's experiences are, but I do know that I had incredible insight into my patients and they with me, because I was open with them. Each visit became a great experience for both of us. People with a disability seem to understand each other. As a nurse, I like to show people how to lose focus on their problems and to believe they can do more than they expect.

I became more interested in nursing after my disability, not so much in the technical skills, but rather in acquiring information and making connections with patients. I developed more interest in anatomy and physiology and in other factual material. I wasn't as interested in simply giving shots. The experiences of my accident and consequent hospitalization stimulated more awareness in the whole scope of nursing.

I'm Catholic and, although I had a very deep faith before my injury, I have grown even closer to God now. I had a few problems with religion when I was injured, and I didn't want to talk to the priest. I had all of the "why me" questions. I received misinformation from a few people, including some Catholic priests. I'm not a traditional Catholic now, like I used to be. I actually spent time at church every day when I was in college, but after my accident, I only went to church a few times. My faith is very important to me and I know my beliefs. My injuries solidified them, they did not break them. But, I'm not practicing any more, and I don't know why because my religious beliefs definitely helped me get through the crisis.

After I graduated from nursing school, I took the summer off, and then, went right into graduate school that fall. I had wanted to attend graduate school in a particular city because many of my relatives lived there. I interviewed at two prestigious universities, one Catholic. I didn't like the Catholic university because of their attitude. My mother was with me, and they treated me as though I were inadequate. The administrator said, "Come through the back door, because the office isn't accessible for a wheelchair. You're going to have to come through the back, because I have to find another room for us." It was a dreadful experience.

I interviewed at the other university, but they didn't have the program I wanted. I found the program I wanted at a university in a different state. It was a wonderful experience. The woman who ran the mental health nursing program, Debbie Patterson, became my mentor. When we met, she told me there would be no difficulties in their accommodating my disabilities.

I did have one negative experience concerning my disability; during a mental health clinical experience the instructor had a problem with my disability. I can't explain it. Even though she worked in the mental health field, she had trouble dealing with my disability and gave me low marks. I went to my faculty adviser, who said she thought this might happen. She asked, "Do you think she's struggling with your disability?" I said, "She's clearly struggling with it. She doesn't know how to take me. When I talk with her about my patients, she can't look me in the eye." This woman had a master's degree in mental health nursing, was running an adolescent mental health program, and could not look me in the eye without getting irrationally angry with me. Other clinical experiences were fine.

In graduate school, I lived in a wheelchair-accessible dormitory suite. Since there were no others with a disability, I had the suite to myself. Later, somebody else was assigned to the suite. She was great and it was a satisfactory arrangement.

My experiences with patients were interesting. In mental health nursing, I was supposed to encourage the people to talk about themselves and, in order to do that, I had to first break down the barriers. Since I was in a wheelchair, as their counselor, I had the right to talk about myself. I would say something about my disability. I worked with many adolescents with substance abuse problems, and they couldn't get over that I was a nurse in a wheelchair. I told them about my accident and school experiences. "I'm doing fine. I acquired a spinal cord injury when I was about your age, but life goes on. This is what happened to me." Once they knew about me, things would be all right and I could say, "Now, let's talk about you." I've tried sessions without providing an explanation a couple of times, but it isn't as successful. In the back of the patients' minds are constant thoughts and questions about me. If I address their unspoken questions, we can get to work on their problems more quickly and successfully.

Children are interesting to work with also. They immediately want to know, "Can you walk? How did you get that injury? Hey, lady, how do you get that chair in the car? Do you sleep in that chair?" They always ask me that last question. I learned, in my graduate program, that answering questions about myself would be an important part of being a counselor.

The other students in my graduate program were great. I didn't have problems with any of them. We had fun. Everyone had his or her own agenda, including me. My disability wasn't an issue, though, for them or me.

After I graduated, I found work in mental health services as a counselor, in both an inpatient hospital and in a nursing home. I kept this job from August until February, and then moved, to be closer to a state-of-the-art rehabilitation center for therapy. Since I had quit my original therapy, I decided some was finally required. I wanted to participate in the walking and bicycling programs. Although I went for that reason, I soon became the clinical coordinator of the program.

After I left that position, I became an educator for a rehabilitation hospital. I participated in all of the education programs primarily for small groups, and did some litigation work as well. Later, I became the Director of Spinal Cord Injury in a hospital unit.

I've only had one administrator who experienced difficulty with my injury, as most have been positive about our relationships. I've had administrators who have said, "We're going upstate in two hours, go get your stuff. I'm putting you in the van and we're on our way." The attitude was "so what if you have a disability." I've known several administrators with outlooks like that.

Accommodations

None of the facilities in which I've worked have had to make special accommodations for me. Since I worked in rehabilitation centers, they were more accessible than other places, but they still needed improvement. For example, if the bathroom in the spinal cord gym was not accessible for me, it would not be accessible for any of my patients. A fight for improvement was not for me, but for my patients. A fight for better parking and outdoor accessibility was not a battle for me, but rather for the people who couldn't speak for themselves.

Most of my professional experiences with nurses and staff members have been very positive, and I have not had trouble regarding my disability. I do know that some people in the medical field have a hard time with nurses with a disability. They don't know if you're as smart, as hardworking, or as motivated as someone who comes to work in a Liz Claiborne suit and leather shoes. Unfortunately, people still judge by outward appearances.

In my last job I was in the field a lot, but I would also go to a hospital to evaluate patients before they could come into the rehabilitation program. Generally, the doctors didn't know me and I experienced a few problems. Doctors and some staff members still want to treat me as a patient, and nurses especially seem to have a hard time treating me as a peer. At times, it can be difficult.

Therapists like to tell me I should do this, or do that. They see my chair and think they should talk about it. I have a problem with my ankle, which was broken in my injury; it looks like it's not aligned correctly. A hospital therapist might say, "Fix your ankle." They frequently make me feel like a child again, and I believe it happens too often. I also hear comments about my chair: "Don't you think you should fix your upholstery? You're kind of ... slouchy."

Doctors stay far away from that kind of thing, but nurses and therapists don't. Doctors don't have much knowledge about disability issues. If doctors think I need physical therapy, they will order it, but they don't know how to do the therapy themselves. I get hyper-reflexive when I have to go to the bathroom. I've had that happen to me while on duty, and a few nurses have looked at me like something's seriously wrong with me. I tell myself, "Nothing is wrong with you. You have to go to the bathroom."

A few years ago, I met an attorney who needed a nurse to do some medical record reviews. I started working for him and then continued on with other attorneys doing the same work. I've been doing this off and on ever since, and now, I want to do it full time. I haven't reviewed very many cases that have gone to trial, though, since most cases die in mitigation. As an expert witness, it is very important how you come into the courtroom and dress. The jury is made up of lay people who judge your credibility by how you look and sound. Since I've had a strong background in education now—educating mostly health care professionals and patients—I can get my points across effectively because I speak like a lay person. I don't use medical jargon because I've worked on my communication with many patients who don't understand technical speech any more than a jury would.

One case I worked involved this man with a low quad—C7-C8—and he weighed about four hundred pounds. As I was speaking in court, I outlined things the man could and couldn't do. It was a life care plan I had written for him. I had the feeling that the members of the jury thought a person in a wheelchair is a person in a wheelchair. I explained to them the difference between a quadriplegic and a paraplegic. Unfortunately, most of our population doesn't see, or understand for that matter, the difference between a person with multiple sclerosis and one with a spinal injury.

Generally, I work with the plaintiffs, but the defense would probably like my expertise better. I definitely have to play up my knowledge and factual accuracy because of my disability. It's actually a lot like talking to a patient in that first, I explain my disability and try to make them feel comfortable. Sometimes, the attorneys ask me about my disability, and if they're comfortable with it, they hear me better. If a petitioner with a broken leg wants $100,000.00 for pain and suffering, and the defendant brings me to court as an expert witness, and the jury sees that I'm a paraplegic, it could get sticky.

Recommendations

If I had the opportunity to speak with a student with a disability considering a nursing career, I would say, "You definitely can do it." It depends on the structure of the program, however, and how narrow or unbending those involved with the program will be. Our greatest barriers are not physical; they're mental. Not every nurse needs to give shots, and not every nurse needs to use all ten fingers. Not every nurse needs to walk into a room. Not every nurse needs to practice in a hospital. There are many more options. I'm a nurse and my office is in my house. I read medical records for attorneys. My knowledge base is strong and I use that knowledge, but I don't have to go to a hospital and turn a patient every morning. I'm still a nurse.

Remarks

Christine describes the importance for nursing students with a disability to find the right program, to break down changeable barriers, and to explain their disability to patients and colleagues. She sees that the greatest barriers are mental, not physical. In a variety of situations, however, she feels that her ability is questioned because of the extent of her disability. She discusses the wide range of opportunities for nursing practice that extend beyond the hospital setting. A standing wheelchair might be helpful for a student or nurse with a spinal cord injury to facilitate observing or working in the operating or treatment room. Additionally, service dogs offer a valuable support for many people with disabilities. Examination tables designed for patients with disabilities may also prove useful to nurses and students with disabilities (see Resources).

Questions to Ponder

- Would Christine have been admitted to the BSN program if she had used a wheelchair at the time she applied to the nursing program?
- Was patient care compromised because of her disability?
- What accommodations might have improved her ability to provide safe patient care?

Individualized Nursing Education Program

An Individualized Nursing Education Program for Christine, developed during her BSN program, might have looked like the following example.

Name: Christine

Date:

Disability:

Nursing student has a spinal cord injury resulting from a car accident. She is a T-4 paraplegic and uses a wheelchair.

Current Performance:

Student has successfully completed the first semester of her junior year in the BSN program. She needs to complete two clinical courses, Community and Home Health Nursing. She has a 3.7 grade point average and excellent clinical evaluations from faculty. A letter from her physician is on file.

Impact on Academic Program:

Student's disability may impact clinical nursing courses, particularly objectives related to nursing skills, such as lifting and bathing patients and performing cardio-pulmonary resuscitation (CPR). She will need assignments to wheelchair-accessible community health agencies and patients' homes. The Office for Students with Disabilities will need to provide accessible dormitory accommodations and remote controls for doors and parking gates. She will also need permission to drive onto the campus.

Assessments:

Nursing faculty assessed the student. Student's knowledge base is excellent. She is aware of her limitations and makes remarkable adaptations. She will need assistance with lifting and bathing patients, reaching, and performing CPR.

Technological Devices:

Student will need access to a computer and software programs that provide opportunities for simulation of clinical skills.

Short-term Goal:

The student will maintain a grade of C or better at mid-term, in all nursing courses. Course work will include examinations, papers, projects, and demonstrations of clinical skills. Clinical skills will be demonstrated in a variety of ways (hands-on, computer simulations, verbal, written) during the fall semester. A plan will be developed for the student to meet the needs of patients who might need CPR. Clinical courses will include a written evaluation by the faculty member, signed by the student.

Annual Goal:

The student will receive a final passing grade of C or better in all nursing courses. Course work will include examinations, papers, projects, and demonstrations of clinical skills. Clinical skills will be demonstrated in various ways (hands-on, computer simulations, verbal, written) throughout the academic year. Student will demonstrate established plan to meet the needs of patients who might need CPR. Clinical courses will include a written evaluation by the faculty member, signed by the student. Student will meet all additional college requirements.

Accommodations, Supports, and Related Services

Faculty Advisor Responsibilities:
- Refer student to the Office for Students with Disabilities
- Refer student to the financial aid office
- Refer student to a state vocational rehabilitation program to explore possible benefits
- Refer student to a local spinal cord injury association
- Refer student to the campus counseling service

Clinical Courses
Objectives related to nursing skills (e.g., lifting patients, turning patients, performing CPR, treatments, medications).

Student Responsibilities:
- Report disability to clinical instructor before clinical experience begins
- Report disability to assigned primary/charge nurse of community or home health care agency
- Find adequate transportation to clinical experiences

- Recognize limitations and seek help when needed
- Work with assigned nursing student "buddy"
- Collaborate with primary nurse, student buddy, and instructor regarding establishment of a plan of action if a patient needs CPR
- Demonstrate knowledge of nursing skills using various methods (e.g., hands-on (when possible), verbal, written, diagrams, computer programs)

Clinical Instructor or Faculty Responsibilities
for Each Clinical Experience:

- Inform community/home health care agency regarding student's disability
- Identify accessible community health care agency experiences
- Collaborate with home care agency staff members to identify patients with accessible homes
- Collaborate with agency staff members and student regarding establishment of a plan of action if a patient needs CPR
- Assign a student "buddy" to assist with physical activities (e.g., lifting patients, giving patient baths or treatments)
- Provide student with diverse opportunities to demonstrate nursing skills (e.g., hands-on (when possible), verbal, written, diagrams, computer simulation programs
- Establish a mutually agreed upon system of communication between a faculty member and the student (e.g., cell phones, pager)
- Facilitate patient, staff and peer group acceptance
- Provide alternate or make-up experiences if needed
- Provide continuous assessments of student's clinical skills and need for accommodations and/or support

Classroom Instruction

No accommodations or supports are needed in classroom situations at the present time. Building and classrooms are accessible.

Testing Modifications:
Computers and software will be available in the nursing laboratory, when needed.

Office of Students with Disabilities
The Office of Students with Disabilities will provide the student
with the following supports:
- Accessible dormitory accommodations (spring semester, main
  campus)
- Accessible classrooms (spring semester, main campus)
- Remote control for doors and parking gate (spring semester,
  main campus)
- Car sticker for on-campus parking (spring semester, main campus)
- Cell phone for clinical courses in the community

Transition Needs
Student may need an adjustable height table or adjustable swivel
arm for keyboard when she takes the National Council Licensure
Examination (NCLEX), after graduation.

Evaluation of Program
This Individualized Nursing Education Program will be re-evaluated at the end of the fall semester or before, if indicated. The student
or a faculty member may request a reevaluation at any time.

Signatures:

Student_____

Faculty Member (s) _____

Dean or
Director_____

Office of Students with
Disabilities_____

Date_____

CHAPTER 8

FEELING AND SEEING WHAT NURSES HEAR
Nursing school with a hearing loss

Patrick has a hearing loss of twenty percent, and tinnitus. He shares his journey from an aircraft carrier in the Navy to nursing school in the South. He describes his experiences in an associate degree program, BSN program, graduate school and his work as an ER nurse.

During the Vietnam War, I was in the U.S. Navy on the aircraft carrier U.S.S. Constellation. The high turbine engines on jet aircraft are notorious for ruining high frequencies in hearing. The navy spent a week testing my hearing and told me I had a twenty percent hearing loss, and that I have problems with the higher ranges of sound.

When I was discharged from the Navy I was told that I qualified for a twenty percent disability income, a significant amount of money. I thought about it and declined, saying, "No thanks. I can take care of myself." I've done that for several years now.

I also have tinnitus, which is a ringing in my ears, and I've had this disability ever since I joined the Navy. The high frequency ringing blocks out noises that are a little higher than a telephone ring. In musical numbers, I don't hear the high instruments. I can hear a regular telephone with a normal ring, but the new cell phones I don't hear at all. I don't hear chalk squeaking on a board, and for that I'm glad because it used to drive me up a wall. I don't have a problem sitting in a room watching a television set or hearing a lecturer. The human voice is low enough that I can hear it fine. Alarms cause a problem though, so I can't use alarm clocks. I've got one of those old tin ones that goes BRING BRING BRING. It literally knocks me out of my bed. I have a pager that vibrates, and if it has a new battery, I can sometimes hear it ring. Even still, I usually keep it on vibrate.

I don't wear a hearing aid, but I probably should. I love to keep everything as simple as I can. I've been doing fine without a hearing aid by compensating in other ways. If hearing becomes a problem, however, I will wear one.

Disclosure

After I was discharged from the Navy, I applied to a nursing program at a community college. I didn't tell the administrators about my disability on the application because there wasn't a place to indicate that type of information; however, we had a written exam and an oral exam in addition to the application. On the oral exam, I told Mrs. Hammon, the elderly lady who was in charge of the program, about my disability, and she questioned me extensively about whether or not my disability would hinder my progress through the program. I assured her that it would not hinder me at all. She said she'd "put a little check mark in the back of my mind," to see how I was doing. I was the first student she had encountered with a hearing problem, so Mrs. Hammon took a special interest in me and said she would follow me throughout the nursing program, to help me through any difficulties I might need to overcome.

We started with about eighty students, two males and seventy-eight females. I don't know if those numbers had anything to do with it, or if Mrs. Hammon just took a liking to me, but I do know she would always ask me, "Are you okay? Are you having any problems?" I have never known, even to this day, if her interest was due to my disability or the fact that I was a male among all those women.

The only problem I had throughout the nursing program was when I worked with the monitors in the hospitals. Beeping monitors tell nurses about a patient's condition, such as when an intravenous medication is finished or a tube feeding is completed. I learned how to work with the monitors through trial and error. A fellow student or a patient would tell me, "Hey, that pump's alarming or, that monitor is alarming." People may have thought that I didn't know what I was doing, or maybe that I needed to pay closer attention. When the instructor and other students realized that I didn't hear the alarms, I knew that I had to come up with a system in order to function, or I wouldn't get through the program.

That's when I learned the alarm equipment also has lights. I tuned into using the lights and looking at the monitors themselves more often. For every time another nurse looks at a monitor, I look at it a few dozen times, because of my inability to hear the alarm. I now know how to set up the equipment in the patient's room to see the warning lights. I've learned to adapt, and I must say that I give better patient care because I am more aware of what is going on in the patient's room. I see more because I have to see more.

Reactions

Clinical courses involve nursing students actually caring for patients in hospitals and other health care settings. The courses are "hands on" experiences. One of my first nursing instructors in a clinical course told me, "As long as you can answer your bells and patient's call lights, we will have no problems." I tried twice as hard because I knew she would be watching, whether I knew it or not. If another student ever told her, "Patrick's alarm went off for five minutes, but I took care of it," that would have created a problem for me. But it never did, because whenever my patients alarms went off I responded appropriately. I was determined to get through the program and into the nursing field.

The vast majority of students didn't know about my disability. I was so aware that I had to do something with a beeping machine that I took care of it very quickly. From the very beginning, a couple of male friends were protective of me. They may have wanted to be friends because there were only two males in the class, and I never asked them, "Are you watching out for me because I don't hear well?" I accepted their help gratefully. I didn't have problems with any of the other students. We were all scared stiff and trying to get through the various courses. No one was too concerned with other people. There were quite a few students in my program and I still see a few of them from time to time. I work with a couple of them now, and, over the years, if they had been concerned about my hearing loss, it probably would have come out, but it never has.

I never got the impression that instructors were cutting me slack and most of my patients were unaware that I had a problem. I did have one gentleman ask me, "You don't seem to use your stethoscope as much as the other students or professional people." I explained to him that it didn't help me much, but the piece of medical "jewelry" did make me look pretty good! Since that experience, I purchased a top quality and expensive stethoscope that helps.

Another patient also remarked that I didn't use the stethoscope much, so I explained my situation. Many times, when I take a patient's blood pressure, I palpate with my fingers while pumping up. This way I can feel blood pressure as well as another nurse can hear it. Nine out of ten people I have told about my way of doing this have thanked me for showing them. I've even gone as far as to pump up and let them feel their own pressure, which allows them to know more about it. It's easy to do and it's a good educational tool. It shows the patient and family members how the human body can adapt to different situations. I have used a digital blood pressure machine, but I always take the first blood pressure manually. It has become part of my job.

After graduation, I started working on an orthopedic floor, before switching to the emergency room. I've been there ever since. There are many alarms at my work site, but I've compensated by using the lights. It is surprising how many professionals don't know that medical equipment often has lights as well as sounds. I don't hear the sounds, but I compensate by keeping my eyes on the equipment. I always position my patient's equipment so that I can see it easily. I am accustomed to seeing these lights. When you have a disability like I have, you learn to compensate quickly.

When I am auscultating a patient's lungs—listening to breath sounds with a stethoscope—I don't hear the high frequency pitches. I can usually hear wheezing. Crackles and rales are sounds made by air passing over airway secretions. I'm not sure if I hear them well enough, but I've adapted my hands by using the "99" technique, which I learned years ago. I place my hands on a patient's chest and ask him or her to say "99" a few times. I've fine-tuned my hands so that I can feel vibrations and pick up consolidated areas in the lungs, like in pneumonia, just as quickly as another nurse can hear with a stethoscope.

Accommodations

The people at work haven't made special accommodations for me, but they do understand that I might rearrange the equipment. For instance, when we are taking care of a patient having a heart attack, there are generally four to six pumps and monitors running. That's a massive amount of equipment on the patient. I arrange that equipment differently than another nurse would, in order to see how they are functioning. Another nurse might place a pump in a position where she can't see it, but she'll hear it. Since I won't hear that alarm, I keep the curtain pulled back, in order to see the patient and the equipment, from a maximum angle.

I take great care of my patients. I don't sit on a stool and stare at them, but as I walk by, I'm always checking things. Since none of the equipment is permanently mounted I can move it any way that is best for me. Actually, most of the staff like the way I do things because they can also see everything at a glance.

I don't perceive myself as having a problem, and I have to say that I have had no problems with anybody on the job. Some of the new nurses on board don't even know I have a hearing problem. I've adapted so well that, unless I tell them I have a high frequency hearing loss or a monitor goes off and I'm not there in two beeps, they won't notice.

I have never felt that my patients had concerns about their care being compromised, except for one isolated incident. Years ago, I was working with a family of black people. There were two young kids, about twelve to fourteen years old, who accused me of being a racist. I was taking care of their grandmother; I took her blood pressure by palpation and then left the room. They complained that the reason I didn't take my time and use my stethoscope was because she was black and I didn't care. Unfortunately, I hadn't taken the opportunity to explain what I was doing and why. I blew off their accusation because it wasn't deserving of a response.

After being a nurse for four years, I returned to school to get my bachelor's degree in nursing. I don't remember if there was a place to indicate a hearing handicap on the application; however, I do remember telling Betty Morelli, the program coordinator, that I had a hearing disability. She was very supportive and said, "If you have any problems, we can work through it." I made it through the BSN program without any problems.

Now, I'm enrolled in a master's degree nursing program in the Family Nurse Practitioner track. I'm taking my last class in geriatrics and have about sixty more hours to complete my practicum. A doctor was concerned that I was unable to hear certain lung sounds and recommended that I call a local medical supply vendor, who might carry a stethoscope that could help me. I called the vendor and got one ASAP. It cost about $200.00. It has made a significant difference in my practice, and in my confidence. I can now hear high pitched sounds! I would recommend this type of stethoscope to any nurse or nursing student with a hearing problem.

I will graduate in May with my master's degree in nursing. The Urgent Care Center at our hospital is staffed with nurse practitioners. I'm negotiating for a position there. I've had two or three doctors approach me about working in their practices. I've also had an emergency room physician contact me about a possible position, and I'm considering some doctoral programs. I want to see what's available before I make a firm decision.

My family wasn't particularly supportive of me. My siblings were married and had kids who needed their focus. They were there when I needed them, but they're not overly supportive people. If I were to say to one of them, "Hey, I need a hundred dollars for registration," I would be given the money. I'm the first person in our family to graduate from college, and I feel it's important for my sister's kids to have someone in the family with a good education. That's one reason I keep going back to school. They need a role model to come to for advice … someone who has been through the hardship of working his way through school and knows a few tricks. I'm hoping they will come to me.

When I reflect on my experiences, I feel good knowing I can achieve what people with normal hearing can achieve. I am proud of my accomplishments, especially when I hear somebody complain that they can't do this or that, because I know they can do it if they have the desire. I wish I could hear as well as other people, but it doesn't bother me that I can't. I'm doing exactly what I want to do with my life. The Lord gives us our brains and it's up to us to use them. We cannot pray our way through nursing school. We cannot pray our way through anything. God gives us intelligence and it's up to us to use that intelligence. That's how I feel about that. Many people say, "Oh, I can't do it," and don't even try. There are a few people, like me, who can do almost anything because we make it happen.

Recommendations

The best advice I could give people with a disability is that, if they have the determination to get through a nursing program, there is a way to do it. I learned in my associate and bachelor's programs that the faculty will bend over backwards to help. They don't push ... they assist. The effort comes from the student. Those who are willing to do whatever it takes to get through the program will get all the help they need. They'll do the work, but the faculty will lead in the right direction. That's one of the most generous things a teacher can do—show a student how to do something and then make them do it. That is a hallmark of an excellent teacher. My instructors have been second to none.

I could have sat back crying in my beer, so to speak, and said, "I'll let the government take care of me." Many people do that, but I have a short fuse when it comes to people like that. Obstacles are no problem, if you take them in hand and work to overcome them. That's why I say I don't have serious problems, because I won't let myself have problems. I wasn't programmed for them. I am proud of myself and of my accomplishments.

Remarks

Patrick shares how important determination and a positive attitude are to his success. He describes the ways in which he compensates for his hearing loss, while providing nursing care. He also states that sacrifice and hard work will be necessary for a nursing student with a disability to get through a program. He found that the nursing faculty offered him a great deal of support.

Patrick spoke about an incident when a patient complained about the way he took blood pressures. He needs to be mindful of the importance and responsibility of addressing issues like this and the need to be proactive in providing explanations regarding his hearing loss to patients and families.

Amplified Stethoscopes

An amplified stethoscope is helpful to Patrick. There are many choices available for people with a hearing loss. Special stethoscopes are manufactured by companies such as Cardionics, Welch Allyn, Agilent Technologies, and Littmann. They can be purchased through local medical supply stores, directly from the company, and via the World Wide Web (see Resource section).

Questions to Ponder

- What accommodations might have helped Patrick in nursing school and in hospitals?
- Was patient care compromised due to his disability?
- What accommodations might have improved his ability to provide safer patient care?
- How could Patrick have better informed patients and families about his hearing loss?

Individualized Nursing Education Program

An individualized nursing education program for Patrick, during his associate degree program, might have looked like the following example.

Name: Patrick

Date:

Disability:

Student has a hearing loss of twenty percent in the higher pitched sounds. He also has tinnitus.

Current Performance

The student is a freshman in the AD program. He was admitted with strong letters of recommendations from the Navy. His oral interview was excellent. He has a 3.5 grade point average in pre-requisite courses. A letter from his physician is on file.

Impact on Academic Program:

Student's hearing loss may impact clinical nursing courses. Of particular concern are nursing skills requiring an ability to hear, such as listening to blood pressures and heart and lung sounds. Hearing monitors, alarms, patients' calls for help, telephone conversations and taped reports may also be affected. Classroom concerns relate to the possible need for front row seating, taped lectures, handouts, a note taker, listening devices, CART reporting services or a sign language interpreter.

Assessments:

Nursing faculty assessed the student. Assessments included an evaluation of his ability to hear blood pressures and breath and heart sounds. Tapes of lung and heart sounds and a double sided stethoscope were used. Student did not hear heart/lung sounds appropriately. He was unable to hear blood pressure with a regular stethoscope. He states that he can hear material presented in lecture courses and that he doesn't need a note taker, listening devices, or a sign language interpreter at the present time.

Technological Devices:

The student agrees to purchase an amplified stethoscope. An amplified telephone may be needed at clinical agencies.

Short-term Goal:

The student will maintain a grade point average of C or better in all nursing courses, at mid-term. Course work will include examinations, papers, projects, and demonstrations of clinical skills. The student will bring an amplified stethoscope to all clinical experiences. A written evaluation from each clinical instructor will be signed by the student.

Annual Goal:

The student will receive a final passing grade of C or better in all nursing courses. Course work will include examinations, papers, projects, and demonstrations of clinical skills. Student will demonstrate the ability to use an amplified stethoscope for heart, lung and blood pressure assessments. Clinical courses will include a written evaluation by the instructor, signed by the student. The student will meet all college requirements.

Accommodations, Supports, and Related Services
Faculty Advisor Responsibilities:
- Refer student to campus Office of Students with Disabilities
- Refer student to the campus financial aid office
- Refer student to area and campus Veterans Affairs office
- Refer student to vendors for an amplified stethoscope
- Refer student to local organization for the hearing impaired

Clinical Courses
Objectives related to nursing skills: listening to heart sounds, breath sounds, blood pressures, alarms, patients' calls for help.

Student Responsibilities:
- Report hearing loss to clinical instructor
- Purchase amplified stethoscope
- Bring special stethoscope to all clinical experiences
- Report hearing limitations to primary/charge nurse on unit of hospital or health care agency
- Position all patient monitors in clear view
- Check on assigned patient every 10-15 minutes.
- Assess blood pressures by palpation and digital blood pressure machine
- Ask instructor or primary nurse to verify student assessments of heart and lung sounds
- If blood pressure is taken by palpation, explain rationale to patient
- Schedule time with lab instructor to review and practice use of "99" when assessing lungs on a patient

Clinical Instructors and Faculty Responsibilities
for each clinical experience

- Inform hospital/clinic charge nurse and appropriate personnel about student's hearing loss
- Provide handouts of information presented to clinical group
- Facilitate staff, patient and peer group acceptance
- Provide ongoing assessments of student's hearing related to clinical skills (blood pressures, heart and lung sounds, monitors, patients' calls for help)
- Assess student's need for an amplified telephone on hospital floors or home care agency

Classroom Instruction
Student Responsibilities

- Meet with faculty member before course begins
- Sit in the front row of the lecture classroom
- Attend all classes and tape-record lecture to ensure that all of the lecture is heard

Faculty Responsibilities for each course

- Allow student to sit in the front of the classroom if needed
- Allow student to tape lectures
- Provide handouts of material presented
- Face the class, enunciate well, and speak at a moderate pace
- List new vocabulary or medical terms on the chalkboard or overhead
- Provide announcements, test dates, or changes in schedule on paper, chalkboard or overhead
- Provide scripts of movies or videos shown in class if available

Testing Modifications
None needed at this time

Office of Students with Disabilities

At this time, student does not require a note taker, listening devices, CART reporting services or a sign language interpreter.

Transition Needs

Student will purchase special stethoscope. No additional transition needs identified at this time.

Evaluation of Program

This Individualized Nursing Education Program will be re-evaluated at the end of the fall semester or before, if indicated. The student or a faculty member may request a re-evaluation at anytime.

Signatures:

Student_____

Faculty Member (s) _____

Dean or
Director_____

Office of Students with
Disabilities_____

Date_____

CHAPTER 9

Nurturing your body and mind
Nursing school with a body cast

Jennifer has scoliosis. She had surgery while she was a student in a BSN program in a middle Atlantic state. She continued in nursing school wearing a body cast. Her journey included additional surgery, difficulty finding employment, and graduate school. She is currently a Doctoral student and practices as a nurse practitioner.

At about the age of fifteen, I was diagnosed with scoliosis, a curvature of the spine. The doctors encouraged me to do exercises and they wanted to put me in traction. As a teenager, I wasn't too cooperative with what they wanted me to do. I said, "Look, let me do the exercises and see how it goes." For a few years the exercises seemed to keep my spine from getting any worse.

When I was in college, in my bachelor's degree in nursing program, my problems really started. The scoliosis progressed and the pain started. An orthopedic surgeon was doing an outreach program, a screening, at the university. A friend of mine, who also has scoliosis, encouraged me to attend the screening. It was like being at a freak show. I saw the worse cases of the disease, and the most advanced conditions. It reminded me of seeing the film, The Hunchback of Notre Dame. For sure, I didn't want to end up like that! The doctors recommended that I have surgery. I said, "Tell me where to sign." I didn't know the risk factors involved with the surgery. I simply knew that I didn't want to end up like those I had seen.

I was at a teaching hospital where they were very interested in opportunities to practice surgery. I was seen for a complete work-up and surgery was scheduled for my winter break from school. It was my second year in a BSN degree program, and I planned to have the surgery, return, finish the spring semester, and graduate with my class. In the event that I couldn't continue, or if I were too sick to return to school, I had a Plan B to put in place.

Disclosure

I met with the dean and let her know I was planning the surgery. I asked her if she had any suggestions for me. She said, "No big deal! No problem. You'll do fine!" That was her comment. I resented the dean from that moment on. She didn't give me the kind of compassionate response I would have expected, like, "We'll talk if you have any problems," or, "If you have any problems, we can attempt to meet your needs," or, "If you need to take an additional semester...." None of those things came out of her mouth. Therefore, I didn't know what to expect. I had never taken care of anyone who had experienced surgery for scoliosis. The dean made it sound like it would be a breeze.

Everything went as planned, as I had the surgery and a rod was inserted in my back. I was in the hospital for a week to ten days, when finally my mother came to pick me up on a Friday and drive me home. On Sunday, she drove me back to college, even though I was still in a full body cast! I was very determined to go on with my life. I lived alone in an apartment, about a mile from campus. I made light of any problems that surfaced because I wanted to get the work done and graduate. I was driven by my desire to graduate and receive my BSN. There was nothing wrong with my mouth and my brain. I wanted to go past whatever physical disability I had.

Walking was good for me and walking was what I did, since driving a car was out of the question. I also had problems with pain, bathing, and sitting. I couldn't always sit in the available chair or desk, and getting in and out of the chair was also difficult.

The professors helped out by letting me sit in the back of the class so I wouldn't have to turn my head. Looking forward, I was able to see everything. One professor felt sorry for me and would occasionally drive me home since it was on his way. A neighbor was also a nursing student, and when we had classes together, she would take me home in her car.

Since I knew that I was going to have the surgery, I planned my course work accordingly. I scheduled community health nursing for my last semester. Community health nurses usually don't wear uniforms. I couldn't wear a hospital uniform because of my body cast. I could only wear casual clothes.

The Community Health Nursing course required that students see patients in their homes. I took the bus for my visits. I was accustomed to walking a mile to and from school, so it wasn't a hardship. My instructor didn't say much to me, except to ask, "How is it going?" She didn't ask anything specific about my disability, so I felt like the others, except, of course, for my clothing.

Reactions

Patients would ask me, "What happened to you? Shouldn't you be the patient?" They wanted to sign my cast and many treated me like I was the patient. They were very compassionate and tried to comfort me. "It's not such a bad deal. You're going to be better when you get out of that cast." I was supposed to be the nurse caring for these people, and they were the ones trying to comfort me.

I have great respect for patients suffering from pain, perhaps more than others do. I'm very aware of the need for medical pain control and other ways to reduce discomfort, such as simply being with the patient. When I was a patient in the hospital the primary nurse who was caring for me was a high school acquaintance. Knowing she was someone I could trust was a great comfort to me.

The other nursing students teased me a lot. When it snowed, they would push me over into the snow bank, knowing I couldn't get up. They would razz me and say things like, "She's a turtle and can't get out of her shell." I had one particular girlfriend who was more empathetic; she would come to see if I was having any problems. She was my closest friend and would take me out to dinner occasionally, and just hang out from time to time. We would go to the movies or see a play, and do other things that didn't require my walking a long distance. I didn't attend the school dances, and that was the hardest part. It was my senior year, a special year, and I wasn't able to date.

What helped me the most was having classmates for close friends. We were looking forward to graduating and becoming nurses. We were all faced with some of the same issues. Our school was a typical college, with drinking and parties a large part of the social scene. The serious nursing students focused on doing their homework and looking toward graduation. I was in a core group that was quite motivated and wanted to do good things. The school supported those of us who wanted to learn, and I had some great teachers.

My family wasn't that supportive. One of the reasons it took me so long to get my BSN was that I didn't have good guidance from my parents or high school guidance counselors. My mother was a single parent and didn't know any better. She hadn't gone to college--no one in my family had gone to college, except some distant relatives—but still made do. I knew that the BSN was what I wanted, and felt family members were keeping me from reaching my goal. I actually won a four-year scholarship in nursing. Right from the start, I wanted to attend a four-year BSN program and move out of town. My mother was not supportive of that decision, which caused stress in our relationship. I did what she wanted: I lived locally and got a two-year associate degree in nursing. My plan was to finish the two-year program, become financially independent, get an out-of-town job, and then work on getting a BSN.

Recommendations

I would recommend nursing students with a disability get regular counseling sessions with a counselor who is specifically trained to work with such students. The counselor could provide ongoing support and guidance and identify any problems that might sprout up. These students may be stubborn and block out a problem, which is what I was doing at the time. If students can get in touch with their emotions, they can free up a lot of energy for other positive things in their lives. I did physical healing work, but no emotional healing work. It caused a major loss in my life- loss of not only time as a young person who was a senior in college, but also of a person who was not in touch with my physical body. I still look back and wish someone had placed me in a counseling opportunity and said, "Okay, this is a major loss to your body's agility, but let's work on healing your whole body, your mind, and your spirit; then your school world will be there. You will be able to do whatever you choose to do." But, I didn't have that important support.

I graduated on time, attended the ceremony, and then went home to spend the summer recuperating. In September, I got a job as a nurse in an intensive care unit (ICU). Within two months of working, the rod in my back broke and I had to have surgery all over again.

The surgery was performed in my hometown and many friends visited me—nursing friends. I can remember the day I first got out of the circle electric bed. My girlfriend, Diane, was there to help. I was as weak and limp as a rag doll. To be a nurse and a patient is very difficult.

I was in a body cast for a year and couldn't get a job, so I had to collect disability. I've come to know that things happen for a reason. I did a lot of self-reflection and tried to use the time as an opportunity for personal growth. Earlier in my life, I didn't have the insight to do that. I was looking forward to being a nurse. I often went to the library to read, and I attended various self-help groups to get emotional support. I did a lot of walking and even went to the beach in my body cast.

I started to apply for nursing jobs while still in the body cast. I was turned down by several hospitals. They all said, "Come back when you're out of your body cast." I used to laugh at some of the comments people made to me while I was looking for a job, like, "Aw, who wants a nurse with a bad back! Be realistic." When you think about it from an administrative point of view, they were right. Who wants to hire a nurse with such a disability? What is the number one injury to a nurse? A back injury.

Finally, a hospital hired me under the condition that I would begin working after my body cast had been removed. Either they were very opened-minded, or very short staffed. I didn't have to ask for any accommodations. Other staff nurses and my patients weren't aware that I had a problem.

One of the nurses I worked with asked me if I was interested in going on for my master's degree. At that point, though, I was just happy to be a nurse. A master's degree wasn't an immediate goal, even though I knew I had a good mind; I also knew that I didn't have a great body and shouldn't risk injuring myself again. The nurse told me some grant money was available, and that the master's program would prepare me to be a nurse practitioner. She explained the role and added that one of the faculty members from my BSN program had gone through the program. The faculty member was my mentor, so I said, "Sure, I'd love to be like her." I worked part-time and went to school full-time. I had occasional episodes of pain related to stress, but nothing that limited my ability to function. I finished the master's program and now I'm enrolled in a doctoral program in nursing.

When I look back, I know I wouldn't have changed anything, although I could have used more emotional support. A counseling opportunity would have been beneficial. I'm still working on things like anger and sadness related to having scoliosis and how it has affected by life. I am involved with the Scoliosis Association; I attend meetings and try to be supportive to others.

Accommodations

It would have been helpful to have some accommodations from the nursing program, perhaps ones that would have allowed me to learn at home. Somebody could have taped the class lectures to allow me to remain at home until I was in better condition to attend in person. Another student could have been assigned to me, not to be responsible for my work, but to offer assistance when needed. I did have people who took me to school and checked up on me, but it would have been better if it had been someone who took on the responsibility of helping me as a class assignment ... a volunteer assignment.

Only one faculty member asked me how I was doing, and that was my statistics professor. Ironically, I hated statistics. Nursing faculty members should be more nurturing and supportive of every student, but especially those who are struggling to keep up with their classmates while dealing with a recent disability. If only one had taken the time, interest, and initiative to ask me if I was having any problems they could help me with, I would have been very appreciative.

The program was an upper division, growing program. The nursing faculty was very focused on getting National League of Nursing approval. Perhaps they were too focused on the program requirements. I don't hold a grudge against them. I simply believe those in the nursing profession should acquire the habit of being more nurturing and vocally supportive, in general.

Someday, I would like to do research with people who have had the same experiences as I, particularly women. It seems to be more of a women's issue than a men's issue, even though scoliosis does affect men. Those who have scoliosis learn to live with the pain or discomfort, just as those with arthritis or diabetes do. I would stress to nursing students and nurses with disabilities the importance of nurturing their bodies as well as their minds.

The physical work endured by a nurse, particularly a bedside nurse, eventually involves aches and pain. Lifting and turning patients in bed and helping them get in and out of bed take their toll on the body. In my work as a nurse practitioner, I try not to do things that will cause harm to my body. I know that if I develop chronic pain, I will have to leave my work. Prevention of injury is important.

Now, I'm very mobile. I can do aerobics, but I'm not as flexible as others. My spine is fused. I do have occasional problems with arthritic pain that is related to stress and repetitive strain from computer work. When I have to do anything physical at work, I get two or three people to help me. So far, so good!

Remarks

Jennifer addresses the need for support from faculty, administrators, counselors, friends and family. She speaks about the need to heal the whole person, body and mind, following a disability. Counseling should be considered to assist a student in working on grief issues related to loss, anger, and sadness. The following concerns and issues that she identified may be important to other students.

Counseling

Most universities and colleges offer some type of counseling services. In addition, a student with a disability should investigate counseling services and support groups that are offered locally by rehabilitation centers. Local disability advocacy groups may also offer support groups.

Clothing/Uniforms

Most nursing programs require students to wear a uniform of some type. Requirements can vary from one program to another. Some programs may require a white uniform of the student's choice and others may require a specific uniform from a certain company. If a student's disability influences clothing options, the student should address this concern soon after acceptance into a nursing program and allow time to find an appropriate uniform or to have modifications made to the required uniform. Prior to purchase or alteration, the students should make sure the selection or modifications will meet with program approval. Ideas for modifications of a uniform may be obtained by examining those done by companies that make clothing for people with special needs. Some of these companies can be found on the World Wide Web.

Transportation

Many nursing programs require students to have a car or other transportation, to get to clinical experiences in hospitals, clinics, and health care agencies. If transportation is a concern, the student should address the issue soon after admission, explore public transportation options, and begin networking with other students about opportunities to carpool.

Harassment

Jennifer was pushed in the snow while in a body cast. This could be considered harassment. Nursing students with disabilities and nursing educators need to be aware that schools, colleges, universities, and other educational institutions have a responsibility to ensure equal educational opportunities for all students, including students with disabilities. This responsibility is based on the Rehabilitation Act of 1973 (Section 504) and the Americans with Disabilities Act of 1990 (Title II), which are enforced by the Office of Civil Rights. Harassing conduct may take many forms, including verbal acts and name calling, as well as nonverbal behavior, such as graphic and written statements, or conduct that is physically threatening, harmful, or humiliating. Disability harassment is a form of discrimination prohibited by Section 504 and Title II and both provide students with grievance procedures and due process remedies (see Resource section).

Questions to Ponder
- How could the dean and faculty members have provided a student, like Jennifer, with more physical and verbal support?
- What accommodations would have helped Jennifer?
- Was patient care compromised due to her disability?
- What accommodations would have improved her ability to provide safe nursing care?

Individualized Nursing Education Program

An individualized nursing education program for Jennifer, during her BSN program, might have looked like the following example.

Name: Jennifer

Date:

Disability:

Student has scoliosis. She had surgery on her spine and is continuing course work in the BSN program wearing a body cast.

Current Performance:

Student is a senior in the BSN program. She was admitted with a 3.8 grade point average from her ADN program. She has a 3.7 grade point average in the BSN program. Faculty clinical evaluations have been excellent. A letter from her physician is on file.

Impact on Academic Program:

Student's back surgery and body cast may impact clinical nursing courses, particularly objectives/nursing skills related to lifting patients, bathing patients, making beds, bending, and performing cardio-pulmonary resuscitation (CPR). Student demonstrated her ability to perform these skills in course work, prior to her surgery. Remaining nursing course work will focus on home and community health nursing. In lecture courses, student will need permission to sit or stand in the back of the room. She may need taped lectures and opportunities to make up any work that is missed. Student will be unable to drive; therefore, she will need to use public transportation or to carpool with other students. Due to her body cast, she will need an adapted or modified uniform. The Office of Students with Disabilities may need to provide a clicker-type opener for heavy doors that are not automatic.

Assessments:
Nursing faculty assessed the student. The student wears a body cast that inhibits her ability to lift patients, bend, and perform CPR. She may have difficulty performing some clinical skills (e.g., administering medications, treatments, chest physiotherapy (CPT), dressing changes, catheterizations). She is unable to drive a car. Getting onto and out of a chair is difficult. She needs a remote control for heavy doors on campus.

Technological Devices:
Student will need access to a computer and software programs that provide opportunities for simulation of some clinical skills.

Short-term Goal:
The student will maintain a grade of C or better at mid-term in all nursing courses. Course work will include examinations, papers, projects, and demonstrations of clinical skills. The student will wear an adapted uniform to all clinical experiences. A plan will be developed for the student to meet the needs of patients who might need CPR. Clinical skills will be demonstrated in a variety of ways (hands-on, computer simulation, verbal, written). Clinical courses will include a written evaluation by the faculty member, signed by the student.

Annual Goal:
The student will receive a final passing grade of C or better in all nursing courses. Course work will include examinations, papers, projects, and demonstrations of clinical skills. Clinical skills will be demonstrated in various ways (hands-on, computer simulation, written, and verbal). Student will demonstrate the ability to implement the plan established to meet the needs of patients who need CPR. Clinical courses will include a written evaluation by the faculty member, signed by the student. All make-up work will be completed by the end of the summer session. The student will meet all additional university requirements for graduation.

Supports/Accommodations/Related Services

Faculty Advisor Responsibilities

- Refer student to Office for Students with Disabilities
- Refer student to campus counseling service
- Refer student to Financial Aid Office, if indicated
- Refer student to a local scoliosis organization
- Refer to local transportation services
- Inform student about campus Student Health Services

Clinical Courses

Objectives related to nursing skills: lifting patients, making beds, bathing patients, CPR, CPT, medications, treatments, dressing changes, catheterizations.

Student Responsibilities

- Report back surgery and body cast to clinical instructor
- Report back surgery and body cast to charge/primary/assigned nurse
- Collaborate with primary/charge/assigned nurse regarding establishment of a plan of action if CPR has to be performed
- Schedule patient home visits with a student "buddy"
- Work with assigned student "buddy" when lifting, turning or bathing patients, making beds, giving treatments, or giving medications
- Demonstrate knowledge of nursing skills using various methods(e.g., hands-on, verbal, written, diagrams, computer programs)
- Arrange for transportation to clinical agencies (carpooling, public transportation)
- Obtain adapted uniform, with program approval
- Make up missed clinical days due to absences within established timeframe

Clinical Instructor and Faculty Responsibilities for each course

- Report student's back surgery and body cast to clinical agency
- Assign student to community health settings near a bus route
- Assign student to patient home visits near a bus route
- Assign student a "buddy" to work with (lifting, turning, bathing, treatments, medications), when visiting patients in the community
- Provide student with diverse opportunities to demonstrate nursing skills (e.g., hands-on, verbal, written, diagrams, computer programs)
- Establish a mutually agreed upon system of communication between the faculty member and the student (e.g., cell phone, pager)
- Communicate with student weekly to inquire regarding her health status and need for additional supports
- Facilitate patient, staff and peer group acceptance
- Advocate for student carpooling to clinical experiences
- Make arrangements for make-up clinical days if student is absent

Classroom Instruction for each course

Faculty Responsibilities for each course

- Allow student to sit/stand in the back of the classroom
- Allow student to tape lectures
- Arrange for extensions on due dates for papers and projects if needed
- Allow make-up examinations if needed

Testing Modifications

Student may need to stand up during an examination, and time extensions may be needed. Computers and software should be available in the nursing laboratory when needed.

Office of Students with Disabilities

The Office of Students with Disabilities will provide the student with the following supports:

• Remote control for heavy doors that are not automatic
• Cell phone for clinical courses in the community

Transition Needs

None noted at this time. Student took the NCLEX examination after graduation from her AD program.

Evaluation of Program

This Individualized Nursing Education Program will be re-evaluated at mid-term of spring semester. The student or a faculty member may request a re-evaluation at anytime.

Signatures:

Student_____

Faculty Member (s) _____

Dean or
Director_____

Office of Students with
Disabilities_____

Date_____

Afterword

Students with disabilities are currently being admitted to nursing education programs across the country. Beyond admission, they are progressing, graduating, passing national licensing examinations, and gaining employment as nurses. Some have pursued advanced degrees in nursing. In a few situations, patient care may have been compromised, particularly when nursing students did not disclose their disability (i.e., blood pressures or breath sounds may not have been heard accurately).

Motivation, determination, and resilience were clearly evident in the narrations of the nurses whose accounts were included in this book. The journey toward becoming a nurse was not easy for any of them as they dealt with pessimistic and negative attitudes from members of our society: institutional leaders, faculty, peers, patients and employers. Unfortunately, there is no magic pill to solve every complicated issue that has been identified. For now, efforts to remedy challenging situations will have to be made by everyone concerned: students, guidance counselors, nursing faculty members, disability services staff, state regulatory boards, and society as a whole.

Student Responsibilities

It is imperative that students with disabilities learn as much as possible about the nursing profession, if they are seriously considering this vocation. They should read many sources of information and learn all the options for employment and their requirements, and then spend time with nurses in the various fields, observing them at work. They should make an honest appraisal of their strengths and weaknesses related to the physical, emotional, and academic demands of the profession. They should ask themselves difficult questions: Can I perform the physical and emotional demands of this profession? Will I need accommodations? If so, are they reasonable? Can I meet the physical and intellectual qualifications of the program to which I am applying? How will I inform faculty, patients and other students about my disability? Am I prepared to face the probability of negative attitudes from faculty, peers, staff and patients? Am I thinking as much about the needs of the patients and my ability to provide care to them as I am about my desire to become a nurse?

Some of the nursing students revealed that they refused to reveal their disability and resented any intimation that they might have one, believing that disclosure was a risk that usually resulted in negative consequences from the institution, faculty members, peers, or employers. It is imperative for nursing students to take responsibility for disclosure of their disability. Through disclosure they can receive the accommodations and supports they need in order to be successful and to properly facilitate safe patient care. Everyone involved in patient care— faculty, staff at clinical sites (hospitals, clinics, health care agencies), the student, and the patients themselves—must be aware of the student's disability, in order to promote and provide uncompromised treatment.

Handling Negative Comments

Nursing students who are admitted to programs need to turn any negative comments from patients, physicians, fellow students and faculty into an opportunity for growth. Students need to continuously build bridges of acceptance, not additional barriers. Keeping a positive attitude and learning from negative experiences or comments from others is important. Negative comments may come from ignorance and should not be ignored. Students need to be proactive and inform others about their disability as soon as possible: explain why a procedure may be done differently from other nurses, or demonstrate how a procedure will be done; describe how special equipment works (e.g. amplified or electronic stethoscope); and practice or rehearse positive responses to negative or rude comments. One nurse who is deaf provides all of her patients with a printed handout of information about herself. She includes a picture of herself and information on how the patient and family can work with her to provide care. Approaches may vary, but it is imperative that the concerns of patients and fellow workers are addressed.

Guidance or Vocational Rehabilitation
Counselor's Responsibilities

The counselor of students with disabilities who are interested in a nursing career, should present a full range of information about the nursing profession and initiate discussions on the physical, emotional, and academic demands. The counselor should encourage the students to research available literature regarding other nursing students with disabilities, and to visit the National Student Nurses' Association Web site (see Resource section). They should counsel about the importance of observing nurses at work before applying for the program, and initiate a careful examination of the students' strengths and weaknesses. They might encourage the students to consider volunteering in a hospital, clinic, or nursing home, or working with the nurse at a camp for children with special needs, spending time with a school nurse, or joining the Future Nurses Club or Health Occupations Students of America (see Resource section).

Counselors should advise students to research a number of nursing programs, examine the admission guidelines and program philosophy, visit the nursing program, meet with the dean or director, and visit the campus Office for Students with Disabilities. The collective information and impressions will facilitate a rational decision-making process. The counselor should also provide adequate resource information concerning auxiliary listening technology, special stethoscopes, and computer programs available for students with disabilities, as well as issues related to special uniforms and transportation needs.

Responsibilities of Nursing Education Programs

Nursing programs need to become more open, receptive, and accommodating to students with disabilities in order to promote full disclosure from students. Nursing educators have a responsibility to follow federal laws, which ensure that students with a disability have equal access to the nursing profession.

Nursing educators are responsible for making admission and retention decisions that promote successful student outcomes, and patient safety. They should uphold high standards for all nursing students. In order to meet this challenge, nursing education programs must utilize enforceable guidelines for admission and retention of students, which are related to essential functions and requirements of participation. They should contain concrete, measurable examples of crucial activities, and allow for the making of modifications, based on a student's specific disability and individual learning needs. Once guidelines are in place, nursing educators must uphold the guidelines in their admission decision and subsequent evaluation of a student's performance.

The nursing program must address issues related to the student's right to privacy, which may be an ethical tightrope, when considering such protection without compromising the patient's right to safe care. At times, the rope may tend to tip in the direction of the patient's rights. Given the life and death nature of nursing practice the "greater good" must be considered.

Faculty members should consider the development of an Individual Nursing Education Program for every nursing student with a disability, similar to those used with special education students in public schools. The plan should be developed soon after admission, with the student and faculty members working as a team. Confidentiality should be maintained.

The student's abilities and limitations should be compared with the core performance standards/guidelines and course objectives. If limitations are noted which hinder the student from performing functions outlined in the standards, the student's individual education program should be modified to note that he or she will be unable to meet the standard (i.e., student is unable to hear alarms or monitors). The program should then include whatever systems the student and faculty will use to develop compensatory mechanisms that address the standard and facilitate learning and patient safety. For example, the plan might state that patient safety will be promoted by alerting hospital staff members regarding the student's hearing loss; the student will develop and strengthen compensatory skills, such as watching monitor lights and making frequent patient visits. Issues regarding special transportation, uniforms, equipment, and additional supports should also be addressed and put in writing.

The Individual Nursing Education Program should be reviewed prior to the start of every clinical rotation. Modifications should be made, based on the student's past performance and the expectations of the next clinical experience. New areas of concern may surface as clinical experiences and expectations become more complex. Goals may or may not have been achieved, and some will need to be changed or modified. Planning for classroom adaptations and accommodations should begin early. If accommodations are needed at a clinical site, a planning meeting should be held with the student, clinical professor, and appropriate staff members before the clinical rotation begins. The clinical grade should reflect the student's performance based on the course objectives and goals as outlined in the Individual Nursing Education Program. The final evaluation should become part of the student's permanent records.

Nursing educators and students should prepare for probable negative attitudes from fellow students and others involved in health care, and might consider role-play and rehearsed responses. Nursing faculty members need to serve as an "acceptance bridge" between students and staff, and students and patients.

Sensitivity training related to disability, should be presented in workshops for faculty and all students as part of the curriculum. Content should inform students and faculty about federal laws, which ensure the right of a student with a disability to reasonable accommodations. There should be a zero tolerance policy for harassment of students with disabilities.

Responsibilities of Graduate Programs in Nursing

Programs that offer master's degrees in nursing with concentrations in nursing education should include content about students with disabilities; those studying to become nurse educators should know the legal rights of students with disabilities, the accommodations required to perform various duties, and the obstacles these students often face.

State Boards of Nursing

As more students with disabilities graduate from nursing education programs and enter practice, state boards of nursing should consider ways that these nurses, with special needs of their own, can practice without compromising patient care. Policies regarding their licensure need clear definition and should be inclusive of both new graduates and practicing nurses. Perhaps special practice needs could be noted on a nurse's license (e.g., hearing loss: needs hearing aid and amplified stethoscope), in the manner of a corrective lens or hearing aid notation on a driver's license. A potential employer can make a more informed decision about hiring an applicant, and make plans for appropriate accommodations, with such important information.

Perhaps the state boards of nursing could request that colleges and universities provide them with a record of a student's disability and the accommodations made for that student. The information may need a review by the state regulatory board prior to the time the candidate sits for the licensing examination and/or is granted a license to practice nursing.

The boards should also consider requiring all candidates for licensure and re-licensure to declare any disability that affects standard practice as a nurse. Functional limitations related to nursing practice should be identified by a team of nursing educators, practicing nurses with and without disabilities, and health care agency administrators. Legal opinions regarding issues of privacy and other potential legal ramifications should be part of the policy package.

Society's Responsibilities

As society moves toward greater inclusion of people with disabilities in all walks of life, we will become more accustomed to being served by and working with them in a variety of professions. For nurses with disabilities to gain greater acceptance, society will need to move toward openmindedness and a realization that a nurse is much more than a worker with two legs, two arms, a strong back, and perfect vision and hearing. The heart of caring comes from a person's abilities, rather than his or her disability. A disability is a natural part of life, for patients as well as for nurses.

• • •

The future promises more and more nursing students with disabilities in classrooms and clinical sites. There is a place for them within the profession, but educators and employers must be aware of a person's limitations in order to make appropriate accommodations that will promote patient safety. The student with a disability must take full responsibility for immediate and frank disclosure, regardless of any qualms about possible prejudice. Dealing with both the qualms and the prejudice is only one more hurdle and will benefit both the student and those with whom the student works and serves.

The nursing students who shared their stories in this book wanted acceptance on the basis of their abilities and intelligence, and the same regard and respect as received by other students. They had to juggle the same school, family, and outside employment issues. They shared similar joys in nursing and pride in their accomplishments and did not want special treatment or attention. They were accepted into nursing education programs and given the opportunity to succeed, and they did.

Solutions to many of the issues discussed in this book remain elusive; the nursing programs for students with disabilities are works in progress. The power inherent in positive nurse/patient and student/teacher relationships will create a ripple effect in changing attitudes. They may be slow to come, but, inevitably, they will. What is certain is that nursing students and nurses with disabilities will continue to pursue careers in this noble profession and, ultimately, change the course for themselves, nursing educators, and patients, through many caring moments that transcend any disability.

RESOURCES

Readers are encouraged to explore the World Wide Web for disability-specific organizations. The scope of the following list is general and not meant to be exhaustive.

Advocacy

U.S. Department of Education
Office of Special Education and Rehabilitative Services
400 Maryland Avenue, S.W
Washington, DC 20202
1-800-USA-LEARN
1-800-437-0833 (TTY)
Web site: www.ed.gov/offices/OSERS/

OSERS provides leadership, by promoting equal opportunity and access to excellence in education, employment, and community living. It has three program areas: the Office of Special Education Programs (OSEP), the Rehabilitation Services Administration (RSA), and the National Institute on Disability and Rehabilitation Research (NIDRR).

Association on Higher Education and Disability
University of Massachusetts
100 Morrissey Blvd.
Boston, MA 02125-3393
(617)287-3880
(617) 287-3882 (TTY)
Web site: www.ahead.org

AHEAD is an international, multicultural organization of professionals committed to full participation in higher education for persons with disabilities. The organization offers a wide array of publications.

HEATH Resource Center
American Council on Education
The George Washington University
2121 K Street, NW, Suite 220
Washington, DC 20037
(800) 544-3284 (Voice or TTY)
Email: askheath@heath.gwu.edu
Web site: www.heath.gwu.edu./

The HEATH resource center is the national clearinghouse on post-secondary education for individuals with disabilities. It disseminates information about support services, policies, procedures, adaptations, and opportunities at American campuses for individuals with disabilities.

Ohio State University
1900 Kenny Road
Columbus, Ohio 43210-1090
(614) 292-4353
(800) 848-4815 (614) 292-1260 (fax)
Email: ericacve@osu.edu
Web site: www.ericacve.org

ERIC is a national education information system sponsored by the Office of Educational Research and Improvement, U.S. Department of Education. Two of the clearinghouses most relevant to nursing students with disabilities include: ERIC Clearinghouse on Adult, Career and Vocational Education (as printed above), and the ERIC Clearinghouse on Higher Education (as printed below):

ERIC Clearinghouse on Higher Education
George Washington University
One Dupont Circle, NW, Suite 630
Washington, DC 20036-1183
(202) 296-2597
(800) 773-3742 (202) 452-1844 (Fax)
Email: eric-he@eric-he.edu
Web site: www.eriche.org

Educational Equity Concepts
National Clearinghouse on Women and Girls with Disabilities
100 Fifth Avenue, 8th Floor
New York, New York 10011
(212) 243-1110 (Voice/TTY)
Email: information@edequity.org
Web site: www.edequity.org

EEC's goal is to increase public understanding of the issues concerning women and girls with disabilities, and to increase the integration of people with disabilities into all aspects of education, work, social, and family life.

Education and Career Information

American Nurses Association
600 Maryland Avenue, SW, Suite 100 West
Washington, DC 20024
1-800-274-4ANA (4262)
Web site: www.ana.org

The ANA represents the interests of the nation's 2.6 million registered nurses. Membership, conference and certification information, publications, legislation and continuing education programs are available on line.

National League for Nursing
61 Broadway, 33rd Floor
New York, New York 10006
(212) 363-5555
1-800-6691656
Web site: www.nln.org

The NLN is the accrediting body for nursing education programs. The site provides nursing testing and exams, books, continuing education, achievement exams, and diagnostic readiness tests.

National Council of State Boards of Nursing
111 East Wacker Drive, Suite 2900
Chicago, Il 60601
(312) 525-3600
(866) 293-9600
Email: info@ncsbn.org
Web site: www.ncsbn.org

The Council provides information about the National Council Licensing Examination (NCLEX), state boards of nursing and nurse practice acts.

National Student Nurses' Association
45 Main Street, Suite 606
Brooklyn, New York 11201
(718) 210-0705
E-mail: nsna@nsna.org
Web site: www.nsna.org

The NSNA provides career advice, a discussion forum, scholarship information, NCLEX study aids, and an online store.

Health Occupations Students of America
6021 Morris Road, Suite 111
Flower Mound, TX 75028
Phone: (800) 321-HOSA
Fax: (972) 874-0063
E-mail: info@hosa.org
Web site: www.hosa.org
HOSA is a student organization. The mission of HOSA is to promote career opportunities in health care.

Testing Services

College Board
SAT Services for Students with Disabilities
P.O. Box 6226
Princeton, New Jersey 08541-6226
(609) 771-7137 (609) 771-7681 (Fax)
(609) 882-4118 (TTY)
Email: ssd@info.collegeboard.org
Web site:
www.collegeboard.com/disable/students/html/indx000.html

The College Board provides special arrangements to minimize the possible effects of disabilities on test performance.

Educational Testing Service
Rosedale Road
Princeton, New Jersey 08541
(609) 921-9000 (609) 734-5410 (fax)
Web site: www.ets.org

ETS provides information about testing accommodations for people with disabilities and how to register for the SAT, GRE and other tests.

Nursing Students and Nurses with Disabilities

ExceptionalNurse.com
E-mail: ExceptionalNurse@aol.com
Web site: www.ExceptionalNurse.com

This web site is a nonprofit resource network for nursing students and nurses with disabilities, nursing educators, guidance counselors and disability service staff. It provides links to disability-related organizations, technology, equipment, financial aid, employment opportunities, legal resources, mentors and research.

Association of Medical Professionals with Hearing Loss
Web site: www.AMPHL.org

AMPHL provides information, promotes advocacy and mentorship, and creates a network for individuals with hearing losses interested in working in the health care field.

Network for Overcoming Increased Silence Effectively (NOISE)
Web site: http://www.amphl.org/noise.html

This is an international electronic mail listserv for medical professionals and students with any degree of hearing loss. To subscribe, send an email to: Listserver@lists.acs.Ohio-state.edu
or visit the web site.

David Wright's Pages: Deaf and Haring Impaired Peoples' Access to Nursing Education
Web site: http://www.shef.ac.uk/~md1djw/

This site provides information for students and nurses who are Deaf or hearing impaired. The site originates in the United Kingdom. It offers information helpful to nurses worldwide.

Promoting Awareness in Healthcare, Medical and Deaf
Web site: http://www.urmc.rochester.edu/smd/stdnt/pahmd/welcome.htm

PAH, MD is a volunteer organization of medical students, deaf and hard of hearing healthcare recipients, healthcare providers, medical school faculty, and advocates.

American Medical Student Association
Web site: http://www.amsa.org/adv/cod/

The committee on disabilities is dedicated to serving as a support, resource, networking and advocacy group for physicians-in-training, physicians, patients with disabilities and their allies. It hopes to identify and change problems which have previously prevented qualified individuals from entering or staying in the field of medicine.

Association of Nurses in Aids Care
Web site: http://www.anacnet.org/leadership/hiv-nurses.htm

The ANAC offers a quarterly newsletter for HIV+ nurses and students.

University of Salford School of Nursing
Web site: http://www.nursing.salford.ac.uk/pioneers.html

This university launched Europe's first nursing course for deaf students.

Service Dogs Invisible Disabilities
Web site: http://www.sdid/

This is an online community comprised of individuals living with invisible disabilities, such as epilepsy, fibromyalgia, multiple sclerosis and psychiatric disorders, that are not readily apparent, who are assisted by a service dog.

Nurseshouse.org
2113 Western Avenue, Suite 2
Guilderland, New York 12084-9559
(518) 456-7858
Web site: www.Nurseshouse.org

This organization offers temporary financial assistance to nurses who are ill, convalescing or disabled, and unable to meet current living expenses.

Discussion Groups

Is there a place in nursing for RN's/LPN's who are disabled?
Web site: http://www.medscape.com

Medscape Nurses (WebMD) hosts a discussion forum for RN's with disabilities.

Disabled and Injured Healthcare Workers
Web site:
http://groups.yahoo.com/group/DisabledAndInjuredHealthcareWor
kers/
This group offers a discussion forum for nurses with disabilities.

Nursing Faculty

Oregon Health Sciences University
Center on Self-Determination
The Health Sciences Faculty Education Project
Web site: www.healthsciencefaculty.org

This project assists faculty to provide effective instruction for students with disabilities in health care professions.

Boston University
Center for Psychiatric Rehabilitation
Web site: http://www.bu.edu/cpr/reasaccom/

This on-line resource offers assistance to employers and educators related to reasonable accommodation for people with psychiatric disabilities.

PEPNet.org
Web site: www.PepNet.org

The Postsecondary Education Programs Network, is the national collaboration of the four Regional Postsecondary Education Centers for Individuals who are Deaf and Hard of Hearing. The goal of PEPNet is to assist postsecondary institutions across the nation to attract and effectively serve individuals who are Deaf and Hard of Hearing.

Northeast Technical Assistance Center
Web site: www.netac.rit.edu/about.html

The Northeast Technical Assistance Center (NETAC) provides outreach and technical assistance to postsecondary programs in the Northeast serving individuals who are deaf and hard of hearing.

Student Financial Aid

Scholarships designated for students with disabilities are quite limited. Students are urged to pursue scholarships related to disability as well as those with criteria other than disability.

Federal Student Aid Information Center
Postsecondary Education
U.S. Department of Education
Washington, DC 20202
(800) 433-3243 (800) 730-8913 (TTY)
Web site: www.fafsa.ed.gov

The Information Center can answer questions about federal student aid.

Alexander Graham Bell Association for the Deaf
3417 Volta Place, NW
Washington, DC 2007-2778
(202) 337-5220 (Voice)
(202) 337-5221 (TTY)
Web site: www.agbell.org

The Association offers scholarships to individuals who are prelingually deaf or hard of hearing and who use speech or speech reading to communicate.

American Council of the Blind
1155 15th Street, NW, suite 1004
Washington, DC 20005
(800) 424-8666 (202) 467-5081
Web site: http://www.acb.org

Scholarships are limited to individuals who are legally blind or visually impaired.

Ethel Louise Armstrong Foundation
Email: info@ela.org
Web site: http://www.ela.org

The ELA Foundation distributes scholarships to women with disabilities who are pursuing an advanced degree at any university in the country.

ExceptionalNurse.com Scholarship Award
Email: ExceptionalNurse@aol.com
Web site: www.ExceptionalNurse.com

A scholarship is awarded to a nursing student with a disability. Preference is given to undergraduate students.

Caroline Simpson Maheady Scholarship Award
Email: ExceptionalNurse@aol.com
Web site: www.ExceptionalNurse.com

A scholarship is awarded to a nursing student with a disability. Preference is given to an undergraduate student, of Scottish descent, who has demonstrated a commitment to working with people with disabilities.

Anna May Rolando Scholarship Award
Email: ExceptionalNurse@aol.com
Web site: www.ExceptionalNurse.com

A scholarship is awarded to a nursing student with a disability. Preference is given to a graduate student who has demonstrated a commitment to working with people with disabilities.

Additional Financial Information/Resources

Department of the Treasury
Internal Revenue Service
"Tax Highlights for Persons with Disabilities"
Publication 907, Cat. No. 15308H
(800) 829-1040
(800) 829-4059 (TTY)
Web site: www.irs.gov

This publication gives an introduction to parts of the tax law of particular interest to people with disabilities. It highlights income, itemized deductions, tax credits, and business incentives. The section on itemized deductions, "special items and equipment" may be particularly helpful.

> Social Security Administration
> U.S. Department of Health and Human Services
> Department of Health and Human Services
> 5 Park Center Court, Suite 100
> Owings Mills, MD 21117
> (800) 772-1213 (800) 325-0778 (TTY)
> Web site: www.ssa.gov

Telephone numbers for local offices are found in the U.S. Government section of the telephone directory. Staff members answer questions about benefits relating to disability, SSI, and SSDI. The Social Security Administration provides benefits to persons with a physical or mental disability that prevents them from working and which is expected to last at least a year or to be terminal. Benefits and services vary in each state.

Rehabilitation Services

Department of Vocational Rehabilitation (VR)

Vocational Rehabilitation is a nationwide federal-state program for assisting eligible people with disabilities to define employment goals and become employed. The VR program is an eligibility program, rather than an entitlement program. Agency titles vary from state to state; it may be difficult to locate in the telephone directory. Contact a state education agency, public library, or the Governor's Committee on Employment of People with Disabilities, to get the number and address of your local VR agency. VR provides medical, therapeutic, counseling, education, training, and other support services needed to prepare people with disabilities for work.

Social Security Online
Web site: www.ssa.gov/work/serviceproviders/rehabproviders.html
This web site provides the contact information for state vocational and rehabilitation agencies.

Department off Veterans Affairs

Vocational Rehabilitation and Counseling Programs
(800) 827-1000
Web site: www.vba.va.gov/bln/vre/vreindex.htm

The Department of Veterans Affairs provides counseling and services to service-connected disabled veterans.

Educational Resources

Captioned Media Program
National Association of the Deaf
1447 East Main Street
Spartanburg, SC 29307
(800) 237-6213 (Voice)
(800) 237-6819 (TTY)
E-mail: nadcvs@aol.com
Web site: www.cfv.org

This is a free loan service funded by the U.S. Department of Education. CFV offers over 4,000 open-captioned educational and general interest programs that do not require a decoder. To qualify for the program, the recipient must have some type of hearing loss or be a parent, teacher, or professional working with individuals with some type of hearing loss.

Library Reproduction Service
14214 S. Figueroa Street
Los Angeles, CA 90061
(213) 749-2463
(800) 255-5002

E-mail: lrsprint@aol.com
Web site: www.LRS-LARGEPRINT.com

LRS produces large print reproductions of educational materials. Each reproduction is made to order to meet the visual requirements of the individual student. The type can be enlarged from 14 to 24 point for postsecondary materials. LRS makes exact copies of original inkprints, made in cooperation with the publishers.

National Library Service for the Blind and Physically Handicapped
Library of Congress
1291 Taylor Street, NW
Washington, DC 20011
(202) 707-5100 (202) 707-0744 (TTY)
E-mail: nlsbph@loc.gov
Web site: www.loc.gov/nls

The library service provides free recorded and Braille reading materials to persons with visual or physical impairments that prevent the reading of standard print material. Contact the Reference Section.

Recording for the Blind and Dyslexic, Inc.
20 Roszel Road
Princeton, NJ 08540
(866) RFBD-585
(800) 221-4792 (Book orders only)
E-mail: custserv@rfbd.org
Web site: www.rfbd.org

This organization provides taped educational books free on loan; books on diskette, library services, and other educational and professional resources to individuals who cannot read standard print, because of a visual, physical, or perceptual disability. RFB&D accepts requests to record books that are not already contained in its 75,000-title Master Tape Library.

Equipment

Special Stethoscopes (hearing loss)

Stethoscopes.com
Web site: www.stethoscopes.com

This web site offers a variety of stethoscopes for people with hearing loss.

Welch Allyn
7420 Carroll Road
San Diego, CA 92121-2334
(800) 535-6663
Web site: www.welchallyn.com

This company distributes a variety of special stethoscopes and medical equipment.

Allheart.com
Web site: www.allheart.com

This company provides amplified stethoscopes for people with hearing loss.

Ultrascopes.com
Web site: www.ultrascopes.com

The pressure sensitive 'Ultrascope" is available from this company for people with hearing loss.

Cardionics Inc.
910 Bay Star Blvd.
Webster, Texas 77598
(281) 488-5901 or 800-364-5901
Web site: www.cardionics.com

This company manufactures the "E" Scope and Pocket Monitor for people with hearing loss.

The pocket monitor provides a visual display of heart and lung sounds on a personal digital assistant (PDA).

One-Hand Blood Pressure Monitors
Web site: www.stethoscopes.com

This company offers one-hand aneroid blood pressure monitors. The pump and dial are attached to the same handle and can be manipulated with one hand.

Listening Devices

Phonic Ear
Web site: www.phonicear.com

This company provides a variety of listening devices for people with hearing loss.

Self Help for Hard of Hearing People, Inc.
7910 Woodmont Avenue, Suite 1200
Bethesda, MD 20814
(301) 657-2248
(301) 657-2249 (TTY)
Web site: www.shhh.org/

This organization provides information about different types of listening devices as well as education, support and advocacy.

Vision Loss

Sight Connection
Web Site: www.sightconnection.com

This company provides talking blood pressure monitors, talking thermometers, and talking scales.

Standing Wheelchairs

Levo USA
Web site: http://www.levousa.com/E/Organis/levoag.htm

This company has been engaged in the development, production and distribution of stand-up wheelchairs.

See-Through Surgical Masks

The Association of Medical Professional with Hearing Loss
Web site: www.AMPHL.org

AMPHL.org provides information about the progress of production and availability of see-through surgical masks.

Examination Tables

Hausmann Powermatic
Web site: http://www.1-medical-equipment.com/Vendors/HAUS-MANN/EXAM.HTM

A Wheelchair Accessible Power Table was custom designed by the late Dr. Sandra Welner for patients with special needs. Model 4450, 4455, U.S. Patent #5507050.

Computers

IBM Accessibility Center
11400 Burnett Road
Austin, Texas 78758
(800) 426-4832
(800) 426-4833 (TTY)
Web site: www.ibm.com/able/

The IBM Center responds to requests for information on how IBM products can assist people with a wide range of disabilities use personal computers.

Apple Computers
Web site: www.apple.com/disability/

Apple provides a wide range of hardware and software to assist people with special needs.

Microsoft
Web site: www.microsoft.com/enable/default.aspx

A wide range of accessibility technology is offered to people with disabilities.

Legal Resources

Office of the Americans with Disabilities Act
Civil Rights Division
U.S. Department of Justice
P.O. Box 66738
Washington, DC 20035-6118
ADA Information Line:
(800) 514-0301
(800) 514-0383 (TTY)
Web site: www.usdoj.gov/crt/ada/adahom1.htm

Office for Civil Rights, U.S. Department of Education

U.S. Department of Education
Office for Civil Rights
Mary Switzer Building
330 C Street, SW
Washington, DC 20202
(800) 421-3481
(877) 521-2171 (TTY)
Email: OCR@ed.gov
Web site: http://bcol01.ed.gov/CFAPPS/OCR/contactus.cfm

OCR headquarters in Washington, DC and regional offices can answer questions on matters related to Section 504 of the Rehabilitation Act of 1973. A state locator box on the web site will direct you to local offices.

References

American Council on Education, (1993), Section 504: The law and its impact on postsecondary education, Washington, DC

Americans with Disabilities Act (1990), Public Law, No. 101-336, 42 U.S.C. 12101

Davidson, S. (1994). "The Americans with Disabilities Act and Essential Functions in Nursing Programs," Nurse Educator, 19(2), 31-34

Davis v. Southeastern Community College, (1979), 442 U.S., 397

Davis, L., Bowlin, L., Hazzard, M., & Futch, L. (1992). "Red Alert: The Americans with Disabilities Act implications for nursing education," Recommendations of a Task Force to the Board of Directors of the Southern Council on Collegiate Education for Nursing (SCCEN)

Education for All Handicapped Children Act (1975), 20 U.S.C. 1400 et seq.

Helms, L.B. & Weiler, D. (1993), "Disability Discrimination in Nursing Education: An Evaluation of Legislation and Litigation," Journal of Professional Nursing, 9(6), 358-366

Individuals with Disabilities Education Act (1990), 20 U.S.C. 1400 et seq.

Magilvy, J.K., & Mitchell, A.C. (1995), "Education of Nurses With Special Needs," Journal of Nursing Education, 34(1), 31-36

Maheady, D. (1999), "Jumping Through Hoops, Walking on Egg Shells: The Experiences of Nursing Students With Disabilities," Journal of Nursing Education, 38(4), 162-170

Manson, J. (1982, August), "Nursing and Medical Students— Admission Policies of Their Schools," Journal of the American Association of Nurse Anesthetists, 50, 409-411

Matt, S.B. (2003) Reasonable accommodation: What Does the Law Really Require? Journal of the Association of Medical Professionals with Hearing Losses, 1. Retrieved May 13, 2003 from http://www.amphl.org/protected/summer2003/matt2003.html.

Rehabilitation Act (1973), P.L. 93-112, Title 5, Section 504, 87 Stat., 355 29 VSC, Section 794

U.S. Department of Education, Office of Special Education and
    Rehabilitative Services (July, 2000), A Guide to the Individualized
    Education Program, Washington, DC
Watson, G. (1995), "Nursing Students With Disabilities: A Survey of
    Baccalaureate Nursing Programs," Journal of Professional
    Nursing, 11(3), 147-153

Index

ABOUT THE AUTHOR

Dr. Donna Maheady is a certified Pediatric Nurse Practitioner and adjunct Assistant Professor in the Christine E. Lynn College of Nursing at Florida Atlantic University in Boca Raton, Florida. She is the author of numerous articles on disability issues, and is also a gubernatorial appointee to the Florida Local Advocacy Committee for Developmental Disabilities. Her advocacy efforts include the creation of a nonprofit web site for nurses and nursing students with disabilities at www.ExceptionalNurse.com. She lives with her family in Palm Beach Gardens, Florida.

Maheady